The Common Chronicle

An exhibition of archive treasures
from the County Record Offices of England and Wales

15 June –11 September 1983

The Association of County Archivists
with the Victoria and Albert Museum

Victoria and Albert Museum

Front and back cover
Illuminated border scenes from the
Hertford Borough Charter, 1605 (**98**)

© Association of County Archivists
and the Victoria and Albert Museum

Published in 1983
by the Victoria and Albert Museum
London SW7 2RL

ISBN 0 905209 42 7

Designed by Graham Johnson

Printed by Gavin Martin Limited

Foreword

The richness of central government archives in Britain has been taken for granted over many centuries. In the early 19th century government surveys began to give an idea of the extent of public records held in each county. But it is only in our own times, since the Second World War, that the work of local repositories, county record offices chief among them, has demonstrated the wealth of archival material that exists to be collected and made available locally.

Historians of the decorative and applied arts are among those who have profited from their activities in the last half century. The production of efficient lists, catalogues and indexes has revealed a vast amount of documentation which allows our cultural heritage to be more fully explored, put in context and better appreciated by an increasingly interested and informed public. The study of decorative art of all kinds, as well as the context it was designed to serve – social, domestic, architectural, and so on – has benefited from sources record offices have made available.

The V & A is, therefore, delighted to welcome this exhibition, arranged by the Association of County Archivists. The Museum has always stressed the importance of developing links with local institutions. Most historical research involves lengthy perusal of archival sources: it may come as a surprise to some that archives are liable to contain documents which can have an aesthetic quality, providing in themselves source material for the study of decorative styles favoured by past generations and currents of change in such styles. It is this aspect which the present exhibition has exploited most successfully, offering visual as well as historical delight to the visitor.

Sir Roy Strong
Director
Victoria and Albert Museum

Acknowledgements

The Association of County Archivists and the Victoria and Albert Museum gratefully acknowledge the assistance of all those owners and depositors who have agreed to the loan of documents for this exhibition.

The preparation of the exhibition has depended upon the effort and involvement of staff in county record offices throughout England and Wales.

Photographic work has been carried out by Messrs. D. Tobias, K. Stubbings, N. E. C. Hammond, R. S. Whitehead and T. James of the Essex and Suffolk County Councils.

Above all, thanks are due to Jennifer Thorp and Wendy Walker whose contribution in assisting Amanda Arrowsmith and Vic Gray in the preparation of the exhibition on behalf of the Association of County Archivists has been enormous and indispensable.

Finally thanks are owed to all those members of the Victoria and Albert Museum staff who have helped with so many aspects of this exhibition and made its mounting possible.

List of Donors and Depositors

We gratefully acknowledge the co-operation of the following owners of documents in allowing items to be displayed in this exhibition:

The Most Hon. the Marquess of Anglesey (**60, 68**)

Mr D. L. Arkwright, Kinsham, Hereford and Worcester (**38, 39, 40**)

Sir John Aubrey-Fletcher, Bt., Chilton, Buckinghamshire (**20, 21**)

Mr E. H. Auden of Goodger Auden and Co., Burton upon Trent, Staffordshire (**152**)

Sir Edmund Bacon, Bt., K.G., K.B.E., T.D., of Raveningham, Norfolk (**69**)

The Rector of Barming, Kent (**30**)

Mr L. Beatty, Cramlington, Northumberland (**125, 126, 127, 128**)

The Bedford Society (**187**)

Bedfordshire County Council (**95, 148, 149, 164**)

Berkshire County Council (**96, 119, 162, 195, 196, 197, 198**)

Revd. J. D. Bickersteth, Battle, East Sussex (**58**)

Major F. H. Blackett, Corbridge, Northumberland (**11**)

The Bouverie Trustees (**212, 213**)

The Rt. Hon. Lord Braybrooke, Wendens Ambo, Essex (**80**)

Bridgnorth Borough Council, Shropshire (**102**)

Buckinghamshire Record Office (**41**)

The Foundation Governors of King Edward VI Grammar School, Bury St Edmunds, Suffolk (**64**)

Cambridge City Council, Cambridgeshire (**101**)

Cambridgeshire County Council (**199**)

The Rt. Hon. Lord Cawdor, Cawdor, Highland, Scotland (**82**)

The Cheshire Constabulary (**167**)

Cheshire County Council (**86, 189, 194**)

The Administrative Trustees of the Chevening Estate, Kent (**70**)

The Church Commissioners (**1, 19**)

John and Thomas Clark, Trowbridge, Wiltshire (**135, 136**)

Clwyd County Council (**147, 151**)

The Hon. David Lytton Cobbold, Knebworth, Hertfordshire (**75**)

Cornwall County Council (**87**)

Cornwall Record Office (**16**)

Mr T. Cottrell-Dormer, Rousham, Oxfordshire (**43**)

The Rt. Hon. the Viscount Cowdray, Midhurst, West Sussex (**55**)

Mr A. M. W. Curzon-Howe-Herrick, Ripon, North Yorkshire (**42**)

Mr Charles Dent, Wetherby, Yorkshire (**5**)

The Rector and Parochial Church Council of Dunstable, Bedfordshire (**24**)

Durham Record Office (**178, 179, 180, 214**)

Dyfed County Council (**165**)

Easington District Council, Durham (**171, 172**)

Essex County Council (**36, 44**)

Mr O. K. Ford, Byford, Hereford and Worcester (**183, 184**)

Messrs Gepp and Son, solicitors, Chelmsford, Essex (**91**)

Sir William Gladstone, Bt., Hawarden, Clwyd (**57**, **142**)

Glamorgan Archive Service (**50a,b**, **61**)

His Grace the Duke of Grafton, K.G. (**89**)

Major N. D. S. Grant-Dalton, St Anthony in Roseland, Cornwall (**84**)

R. Gwynne and Sons, solicitors, Dawley, Telford, Shropshire (**117**, **201**)

Mr N. G. Halsey, Great Gaddesden, Hertfordshire (**79**)

Hampshire County Council (**9**)

Mr E. J. B. Hardcastle, Wadhurst, East Sussex (**3**)

Lieut. Colonel J. C. E. Harding-Rolls M.C., D.L., Rockfield, Gwent (**33**, **144**, **200**, **217**)

The Rt. Hon. Lord Hatherton (**215**)

Henlow Parish Council, Bedfordshire (**10**)

Messrs Hepper Watson and Sons, Leeds (**188**)

Hereford and Worcester Record Office (**62**)

The Rt. Hon. Lord Hertford, Alcester, Warwickshire (**73**)

Hertford Town Council, Hertfordshire (**98**)

Hertfordshire Record Office (**53**, **54**, **76**, **77**)

Humberside County Council (**25**, **202**)

Mr M. Noel Humphreys, Llandudno, Gwynedd (**134**)

The Rt. Hon. Lord Hylton, Bath, Avon (**120**)

Ipswich Borough Council, Suffolk (**4**)

Mr J. L. Jervoise, Herriard, Hampshire (**154**)

The Rt. Hon. Lord Joicey, Berwick upon Tweed, Northumberland (**34**)

Kent County Council (**59**, **81**)

Kirklees Metropolitan Council, West Yorkshire (**203**)

Sir Berwick Lechmere, Bt., Hanley Castle, Hereford and Worcester (**71**)

Leeds Archives Department, West Yorkshire (**46**, **47**, **48**)

The Board of the Grand Theatre, Leeds (**211**)

Leicestershire County Council (**105**, **182**, **204**)

Lincolnshire Archives Office (**6**)

Greater London Council (**155**, **156**, **157**, **158**, **159**, **160**, **161**)

The Rt. Hon. the Earl of Lonsdale, Askham, Cumbria (**85**)

The Governors of Loughborough Endowed Schools, Leicestershire (**190**)

Mann Egerton and Co. Ltd., Leicester (**218**)

Mr W. McKnight Bell, Curwen and Co., Workington, Cumbria (**92**)

The Chief Constable, West Mercia Police, Worcester (**145**, **146**)

The Owners of the Middlesbrough Estate (**93**)

Sir Stephen Middleton, Bt., Belsay, Northumberland (**45**)

The Vicar and Parochial Church Council of Mirfield, Yorkshire (**32**)

Mortimer West End Parish Council, Hampshire (**140**, **141**)

The National Maritime Museum, London (**107**, **108**)

The National Portrait Gallery, London (**216**)

The National Trust (**56**)

The National Union of Hosiery and Knitwear Workers, Leicester (**106**)

Norfolk Record Office (**37**)

The Norfolk Record Society (**22**)

The North of England Institute of Mining and Mechanical Engineers, Newcastle upon Tyne (**121**)

The Northamptonshire Record Society (**83**)

Northumberland Record Office (**129, 130, 131**)

Mr B. Oake, Headington, Oxfordshire (**208**)

The Trustees of the Orford Town Trust, Suffolk (**2**)

The Divisional Manager, Anglian Water Authority, Great Ouse River Division, Cambridge (**8**)

Mr A. Parish, Hoyland Common, South Yorkshire (**133**)

Miss A. Pegrum, Harlow, Essex (**166**)

Major Sir William Pennington-Ramsden, Bt., Ravenglass, Cumbria (**49, 50**)

The Rt. Hon. Lord Petre, Ingatestone, Essex (**51, 52**)

Harris Library, Museum and Art Gallery, Preston, Lancashire (**139**)

The Rt. Hon. Lord De Ramsey, Abbots Ripton, Cambridgeshire (**78**)

Lady Ravensdale (**94**)

Reading District Council, Berkshire (**169**)

The Dean and Chapter of Rochester, Kent (**63, 74**)

Miss I. M. Rosewarne, Perranporth, Cornwall (**132**)

The Royal Philanthropic Society (**109, 110, 111**)

The William Salt Library, Staffordshire (**23**)

Skipton Castle Estates Limited (**137**)

Somerset Archaeological and Natural History Society (**7**)

The Rt. Hon. the Earl of Stradbroke, R.N. (Retrd.), Henham, Suffolk (**31**)

Mrs Violet Stradling, Landford, Wiltshire (**209, 210**)

Messrs. Stanton, Croft and Co., solicitors, Newcastle upon Tyne (**124**)

The Rector and Parochial Church Council of Staveley, Derbyshire (**103**)

Suffolk County Council (**17, 18, 72, 143, 191, 192, 193**)

Surrey County Council (**112**)

East Sussex County Council (**185, 186**)

East Sussex Record Office (**26, 27**)

West Sussex Record Office (**28, 29, 113, 114**)

The Director of Social Services, Chichester, West Sussex (**115**)

The Corporation of Tenterden, Kent (**100**)

The Tetbury Feoffees (**97**)

The Chief Constable, Thames Valley Police (**153, 163, 168, 170**)

Baron Tollemache, Helmingham, Suffolk (**12**)

Tyne and Wear County Council (**116**)

The Town Council of Wallingford, Berkshire (**99**)

Messrs Warrens, solicitors, London (**90**)

Waterside Plastics, Todmorden, Lancashire (**104**)

Mr A. J. Wilson, Banks, Wilson, Brindle and Co., Preston, Lancashire (**65, 66, 67**)

Wiltshire County Council (**150**)

Mr P. C. Withers, Reading, Berkshire (**205, 206, 207**)

The Curator, Worsbrough Mill Museum, South Yorkshire (**122, 123, 181**)

Yorkshire Archaeological Society (**15, 35**)

Yorkshire Archaeological Society, (Slingsby papers) (**88**)

South Yorkshire County Council (**118, 138, 173, 174, 175, 176, 177, 219, 220, 221, 222, 223**)

This list has been compiled from information supplied by individual county record offices.

Plate I Part of the map of the manor of Hammerden, Ticehurst, Sussex, 1614 (**3**)

Plate II Illuminated capital letter from the Bury St Edmunds Psalter, showing the opening of Psalm LII with David and a jester, early 15th century (**64**)

Plate III Section from the Cornwallis Pedigree showing the miniature portraits of Thomas Cornwallis and his wife, Anne Jerningham, 1560 (**80**)

Plate IV Section from the Vaughan Pedigree of Golden Grove, showing Howel, King of All Wales, 1641 (**82**)

Introduction

There was a time when a phrase like 'Our Nation's History' would conjure up, almost without fail, a quick succession of images – Canute on the Beach, Harold struck by the Arrow, the Armada in Retreat, the Great Fire of London, Nelson at Trafalgar – history by pageant tableaux. This will no longer do. Our perspectives have multiplied, our sense of the complexities of society has overwhelmed the simpler view. History can no longer be encapsulated in these technicolour bubbles and the centre of historical studies has shifted away from the court and the battlefield towards the recognition that a national history is a corporate and collective matter in which the people, seen both individually and together, are the leading players.

This 'history from the grass roots' has been slow in achieving respectability. For the Victorians, an interest in the fine detail of our ancestors' lives was more appropriately labelled antiquarianism than history; it was the pursuit of the dilettante, his findings more 'quaint' and 'curious' than significant. Yet it is from this tradition, placed on surer foundations and built up by contact with the skills and disciplines of the economic historian, the demographer, the statistician and others, that an approach has developed which sees the country as the sum of its parts and looks amid the minutiae of local life for the true pulse of the nation.

Indeed, since the 2nd World War, it has been from this area of close analytical study of individual localities and their features that many of the most significant advances in historical methodology and many reappraisals of long cherished assumptions have come. Whether we look at our ancestors' standard of living or their moral and spiritual outlook, their life expectancy or their economic expectations, it has been research at the local level which has refined, and in some cases overturned, our earlier thinking.

Such localised research is, of course, dependent upon the survival and availability of local sources of evidence. It has been the gradual opening up of these hidden, often unsuspected, veins of written history which has fuelled scholarly development. The records of the state became increasingly accessible to historians with the completion and opening of the Public Record Office in 1858. This tremendous wealth of material reflected the degree to which the network of central government had, across the centuries, impinged upon the lives of every town and village, through the workings of the courts of law, the collection of taxes and levies and the oversight of local administration. But there remained, and remains, a vast and important body of written history, outside the bounds of the 'public records', in the form of working documents and personal papers compiled by individuals and institutions in every locality. The establishment of the Royal Commission on Historical Manuscripts in 1869 'to make enquiry as to the existence and location of manuscripts ... of value for the study of history' was a bold attempt to unearth this great submerged stratum of our past. Nevertheless, the resources for investigation have always been limited and the range of archives – from great houses and from borough and cathedral muniment rooms – revealed in the series of Appendices to the Secretary's Reports, although spectacular, could represent only a small percentage of a scattered and still largely unexplored wealth of material.

There remained, moreover, the problem of preservation. Though unequipped with modern knowledge of conservation needs and methods those early inspectors who, on behalf of the Commission, delved into dark cellars and dusty cupboards, must have frequently witnessed the ravages to which time and negligence were subjecting the manuscripts they carefully detailed. Outside the British Museum and the major libraries, there existed no adequate repositories for collections as large (often tens of thousands of individual papers and volumes are involved) or as complex as these. The local library or museum might, and sometimes did, provide a home but the allocation of adequate time and resources to the task of cataloguing and conserving still posed substantial problems.

It was with the establishment of the first county record offices that a happy solution presented itself. Every County or Shire Hall contained a muniment room for housing the records of the Court of Quarter Sessions, the central administrative records of the county, in the care of the Clerk of the Peace. At a time when the break-up of the large country estate was so often placing such collections under threat of dispersal or loss, it seemed a natural progression to extend that care to other archives of historical significance to the area. Bedfordshire County Council set a precedent in the years before the 1st World War which was quickly followed after the War by others – Hertfordshire, Middlesex, Surrey, and so on with ever increasing momentum. So it was from this modest enough inspiration that the county record office movement grew. It was nurtured, from the first, by the enthusiasm of local pioneer archivists and the recognition by interested councillors (in whose keen support and involvement county archive services have always been particularly fortunate) of a responsibility for their county's heritage.

Today, almost without exception, each English and Welsh county has its own archive service, together receiving some 200,000 research visits each year and housing a volume of manuscript history as great as that of the Public Record Office and the British Library together.

The range of archives is unrivalled. Into the county offices have flowed a tide of papers from the estate offices of country houses, from the chests and coffers of cathedrals and parish churches, from the filing rooms of local businesses and councils, from the basements of solicitors' offices and estate agents and from countless individuals who, with great public spirit, have made valued family papers available for study. The forms in which the evidence is cast are many: maps, letters, diaries, minute books, accounts, court rolls, registers, charters, all play their part. Each speaks with its own unique voice, communicating some original element – large or small, more or less significant – to the total pool of information upon which the researcher can draw.

It is perhaps in the very workaday origins themselves of so many of these documents that their particular quality lies, in the disparity between the humdrum intentions of their authors and the weight which the passing of time has placed upon their words. So often, this is history glimpsed out of the corner of the eye, unwittingly set down for future generations by people who would not for a moment have seen themselves as caught up in so remote, abstract or large a tide as that of history. Yet it is none the less significant for that, for in the pauper examination, the Victorian school syllabus or the printed propaganda for a local strike we encounter the essence of past lives, unfiltered by an 'official view' and unadulterated by historical interpretation.

This exhibition does not take as its principal goal the bringing together of the 'best' of this great diffused heritage of written history (whatever 'best' may mean). Nor yet does it seek to embrace the whole range of archives available in county record offices. In two of the three sections of the exhibition, 'The Rural Record' and 'Urban Themes', its primary aim is to capture and convey something of the way in which these documents communicate with us today. In some cases it is the shock of immediacy which impresses, the recognition of experiences and aspirations which bridge centuries in an instant. In others it is the form and decoration which make their mark on us and a second intention, particularly in the section entitled 'Pages of Beauty', has been to indicate the sheer beauty of some of the documents which have reached county record offices over the past half century. The motives behind the creation of individual archives are as diverse as the items itselves. In most cases they ae working products of individual or corporate activity. Few are without practical purpose. Even the most elaborate pedigree is, at core, a functional document. Yet, time and time again, the mere act of setting down a record for future readers, of creating information which, for legal or evidential reasons, must last, brings in its wake the desire to enhance and embellish. With hindsight, we can see the refinement of the finish as an indicator put down to establish the significance of the content of an archive, to single it out for attention from its more humdrum shelf-fellows in the muniment room. The elaborate binding, the extravagant marginal ornamentation, the decorated initial, all carry this weight of purpose aside from the purely aesthetic motive behind their creation. While the medium cannot be fairly said, in this context, to be the message, it is undoubtedly an element in it and we must look at the document as a whole – material, form, content and elaboration – to understand fully the mind and intention of its creator.

Perhaps because they do not fit easily into any category, the place of archives in the decorative arts has been widely overlooked, at least in the post-medieval period. Yet there are here long-sustained traditions with their own conventions and patterns of development which would repay closer attention. Manuscript illumination, for instance, lingered on in charters and manorial surveys long after the advent of printing had quenched the decoration of literary and religious texts. The growth of local map-making in the 16th century provided a medium for creative ornamentation by amateur and professional cartographers in every corner of the country. A tremendous corpus of maps survives with a rich and largely unexplored thesaurus of decorative elements that may be set alongside other great traditions of, for example, wood carving or monumental masonry. In the formal and legal instruments and volumes, particularly of the 17th and 18th centuries, skills and styles of calligraphy persisted while personal handwriting elsewhere declined.

The achievement of the last half century has, by any reckoning, been a major one. The local record office movement has brought to the surface a second history to set alongside the great national collections of state and literary archives. The alarming rate of slow decay and wilful destruction has been largely (though sadly not wholly) stemmed. New perspectives, new avenues of thought have been opened up for exploration. 'The Common Chronicle' is, to an extent, an attempt to present a picture of this achievement; but it is also a celebration of many ordinary individuals, through the records they created, a chronicle of largely unsung characters whose lives, work and activities have left no trace beyond that which has been rescued and is now preserved in record offices throughout the country.

The Rural Record

1 Survey of the estates of the Bishop of Hereford, 1581
Parchment, ink, colour 31.5×38.5 cm
Hereford and Worcester Record Office AA59

A written survey of the Bishopric estates, compiled by Swithun Butterfield for John Scory, Bishop of Hereford, 1559–1585. A fine example of the late Elizabethan development of a medieval type of estate record, enhanced by an unusual degree of illumination in the introduction and final pages. Borders of flowers, birds and insects are employed and each section of the survey opens with an illuminated capital bearing the initials SB. The arms of Butterfield are shown at the beginning and end, together with verses extolling the virtues of his patrons and the quality of his own work.

2 Survey of the Suffolk estates of Sir Michael Stanhope, 1600–2
Parchment, ink and colour wash, leather bound 39.5×54.5 cm
Suffolk Record Office EE5/11/1

One part of a two-volume survey compiled for Stanhope by John Norden. Norden's reputation as a cartographer rests largely on his embryonic *Speculum Britanniae* with its projected series of county maps, but in his work as a maker of estate maps he exemplifies a newly emerging profession. He was clearly respected in this rôle in court circles, at one time acting as surveyor of crown woods and forests. The Stanhope survey of estates in and around Orford typifies the late-Elizabethan transitional phase: a written table of properties, descendant of the medieval survey, introduces the volume, but now complements the estate map, which was gradually to supplant the survey tradition.

1

3 Map of the Manor of Hammerden, Ticehurst, Sussex, 1614
Parchment, ink, colour 90×74 cm
East Sussex Record Office SAS/CO/d3

Colour plate I

Typical of the best estate maps of the period in its combination of exuberant decoration and refined techniques of surveying and representation. The manorial demesne, the subject of the map, is shown as a fine mosaic of small enclosed fields and woodland while the surrounding landscape of the Weald is depicted with lively figures of cattle, sheep, horses and deer. The arms of current and former lords of the manor decorate and surround the map, together with an elaborate strapwork cartouche and scale-marker. The head of Anthony Apsley, lord of the manor and commissioner of the map, is incorporated in the cartouche.

    Executed by William Gier, who was responsible for other maps in the area but of whom little is known.

4 Elizabethan surveyor, Suffolk, 1591
Black and white photographic copy
Suffolk Record Office C14/1

A figure of a surveyor from a map by John Darby of lands in Kirton and Falkenham, Suffolk. Like many Elizabethan cartographers working at the local level, little is known of Darby, although his hand can be identified in a number of maps from East Anglia, characterised by the quality and humour of his incidental pictorial representations. The surveyor on this map carries the tools of his trade while enjoying with gusto a break from his labours.

5 The Whixley Cartulary, 14th-15th century
Parchment, ink, wooden boards, leather-covered 15×23 cm
West Yorkshire Archive Service: Yorkshire Archaeological Society DD 59

Written in a series of 14th and 15th century hands and still in its original binding, this volume combines the medieval cartulary form, with its copies of charters and other significant legal instruments, with an extent or survey, detailing individual holdings in the manor of Whixley, North Yorkshire.

    The cartulary provides an interesting illustration of the medieval method of land division known as 'solskifte', found in areas of both England and Scandinavia. Strips or 'selions' in the open fields were allocated to tenants according to the way they lay in relation to the course of the sun across the sky. The names of the tenants are listed here in the order in which their selions lie in Nethermerssh and Overmerssh.

6 Bassingham enclosure petition, 1629
Paper, ink 14.5×19.5 cm
Lincolnshire Archives Office. Misc. Dep. 264/2

The effects of the enclosure of open fields in this country over a period of centuries are undisputed but an insight into the motives which might induce a farming community to seek enclosure is provided by an unusual booklet, in which the Countess of Warwick is petitioned by her 'poore tenants' in Bassingham, Lincolnshire. The charming sketch-map shows the village stretching along the edge of the open fields with their patchwork of strips. Along the right-hand edge is the six-mile route around the parish boundary along which the villagers' cattle had to be driven to pasture, a journey which 'sore beates theire feete, and impoverisheth them'.

6

7 Sedgemoor Bill broadsheet, 18th century
Paper, printed 32×44 cm
Somerset Record Office DD/SAS S/416/5

The great areas of common land, such as King's Sedgemoor in Somerset, played an important rôle in the lives of those who enjoyed rights upon them. In the late 18th century Sedgemoor was a boggy morass of poorly drained land but Bills to drain it, presented to Parliament in 1772, 1776 and 1788, were all opposed by the commoners who feared deprivation and underhand motives on the part of the promoters.

The broadsheet was for many centuries the anonymous voice of local opinion, expressed sometimes scurrilously, sometimes with biting wit. This broadsheet rejoices in the failure of one of the Bills. 'His lordship' in stanza eleven may be Lord Bolingbroke whose support of the 1776 Bill was based on the need to raise money to pay his gambling debts.

8

8 Accounts of the Bedford Level Corporation, 1665–7

Paper, ink, black and red, parchment bound 29.5 × 44 cm
Cambridgeshire Record Office R59/31/19/8

A finely embellished volume of accounts of the Corporation, more correctly styled the
Governor, Bailiffs and Commonalty of the Company of the Conservators of the Great Level of
the Fens. The ornate finish to a mere financial record reflects the confidence of the body in the
national and local significance of its rôle and work. Created by statute in 1663, the Conservators administered an area of reclaimed fenland and newly constructed drains and rivers
covering 300,000 acres, thus operating on a scale hitherto unknown in this country.

9 Surveying exercise book, Odiham, 1800

Paper, ink, colour 20 × 48 cm
Hampshire Record Office 14M61

An exercise book labelled 'W. Lawrence his Book Odiham School The Complete Art of Land
Measuring Taughte by W. Lee 1800'. No other trace of this school survives but it was probably
one of the growing number of specialist schools offering skills to the commercial classes,
including the now well established profession of land surveying, carried out by a network of
locally based practitioners.

The book consists of a series of calculations of area and drafts for maps. Their inexperience
and lack of polish is clear but their attention to detail is shown in the doves hovering around an
elevated dovecote, a touch which harks back to the 17th century.

South View of the Buildings on Outon's Tenement.

12

10 Henlow enclosure map, 1798

Colour photograph
Bedfordshire Record Office MA 5/1

A section from the map compiled for the Commissioners for the Enclosure of lands in Henlow,
Bedfordshire. The spate of Parliamentary Enclosures in the late 18th and early 19th centuries
provided a great deal of work for provincial surveyors, in this case John Goodman Maxwell of
Spalding.

    The map is unusual in its inset depiction of an 18th century surveyor at work with his two
assistants in the open fields of Henlow. They are using sighting instruments in the form of
stakes, each surmounted by a small open square. The picture is framed by a surveyor's chain.

11 Map of High Hall Farm, West Matfen, *c*. 1760

Parchment, ink, colour 21 × 19 cm
Northumberland Record Office NRO.685

One of a series of twenty-five maps, by an anonymous surveyor, of farms on the estate of the
Blackett family of Matfen, Northumberland. In its finish and detail it typifies the best skills of
the estate mapmaker, which reached a peak in the second half of the 18th century. Textures are
used to indicate differing land uses and shadow is carefully applied to trees to give a sense of
depth. The cartouche itself has become an exercise in creative and individualistic styling.

12 Tollemache estate survey, Cheshire, 1794

Paper, ink, leather bound 11.5 × 17 cm
Cheshire Record Office DTW/2477/B/28

A late descendant of the Elizabethan survey-with-maps, (see 2), this volume was compiled for
Wilbraham Tollemache by Joseph Fenna, one of Cheshire's most proficient 18th-century
surveyors. As a predominantly absentee landlord, Tollemache would have welcomed the
detail provided by a format combining plan, elevation, table and description for each part of
the estate. The overall result is both charming and unusually revealing for the student of
vernacular architecture.

13,14 Norden's 'Description of Essex', 1594
Paper, ink, colour
13 31×22.5 cm (map)   14 18×23 cm (text)
Essex Record Office D/DMs P1

John Norden's *Speculum Britanniae* was among the more ambitious of Elizabethan attempts to provide a national series of county histories or gazetteers. 'Authorised and appointed by Her Majesty to travil through England and Wales to make more perfect descriptions, charts and maps,' Norden in fact only published two county sections. Manuscripts of five others are known to have survived, including the text for Essex, in four versions, and the original of the accompanying map. Norden's historical detail and contemporary economic and social information helped to set the model for subsequent county historians.

15 Yorkshire church notes, 18th century
Paper, ink, wash, parchment covered boards 24×39 cm
West Yorkshire Archive Service: Yorkshire Archaeological Society Ms 338

One of a series of sixty volumes compiled by John Hatfield Kaye (1722–1804), of Hatfield House near Wakefield, for a projected history of Yorkshire.

The compilation of a comprehensive county history was the ambition of local topographers and antiquaries throughout the 17th and 18th centuries. Large quantities of notes were amassed and the collections of earlier scholars coveted and copied. Kaye's volumes are typical. His notes draw heavily on the work of the earlier Yorkshire antiquary, Roger Dodsworth (1585–1684), and William Dugdale, with new material interpolated by Kaye himself.

16 Diary of a Cornish journey, 1795
Paper, ink, vellum-bound 14×21 cm
Cornwall Record Office AD 43

The personal discovery of the British landscape and people, if considered less worthy than the Grand Tour, was nevertheless pursued with increasing vigour by the middle classes as the 18th century progressed. The accompanying travel journals now give a valuable insight into the life of the time. This journal records a journey undertaken, probably by a Mr Guillebard and his wife and daughter, into Cornwall in May 1795. He records distances travelled, the state of the roads, scenery, weather, local industry, and comments on towns and villages visited.

17 Blythburgh Church, early 19th century
Paper, ink, watercolour 34×24 cm
Suffolk Record Office HD 480/6

Isaac Johnson (1754–1835) carried on a successful land surveying business in Woodbridge, Suffolk, for over 50 years. However, it was the combination of his skill as a watercolour artist and his life-long fascination with topography which produced a quantity of sketches of churches, houses, trees and architectural antiquities. Some were worked up as details on his plans, others were sold as individual drawings or in sets supplied to 'persons of antiquarian taste.' His meticulous style produced not only attractive sketches but valuable pieces of evidence for the local historian.

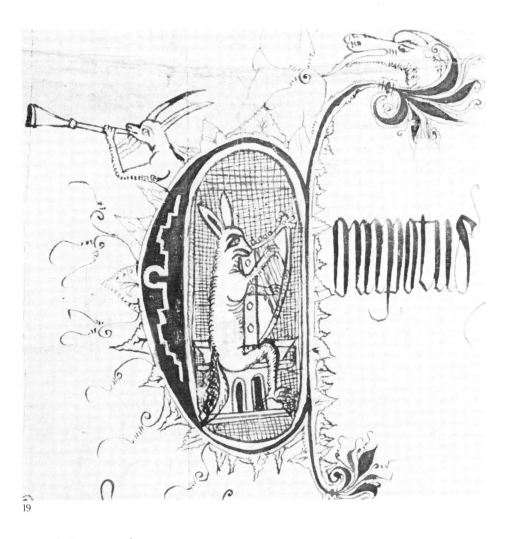

19

18 Francis Grose, antiquary

Black and white photographic copy
Suffolk Record Office HD 480/2

Captain Francis Grose (*c.*1731–1791), the author of *Antiquities of England and Wales,* was one of the most dedicated 18th century recorders of antiquities. Like many of his fellow topographers, he left a collection of scattered notes and drawings, a number of which have found their way into local record offices. Grose is seen here in a steel engraving by J. Rogers after J. M.Wright, published by George Vertue, in 1842.

19 Winchester Pipe Roll, 1336–7

Parchment, ink 53×87 cm
Hampshire Record Office Eccls. II/159348

The manor was the basic economic unit of the medieval estate. The lands of the Bishop of Winchester stretched across southern England from Somerset to Surrey and the annually compiled accounts of the estate took the form of a parchment roll, the Pipe Roll, arranged in sequence of manors. The rolls begin in 1208, and are the earliest known extant estate accounts in the country. The membrane for 1336–1337, which opens with the manor of Taunton, is individualised by the casual but flamboyant decoration of the heading and the fire-breathing dragon, which brings it to a close.

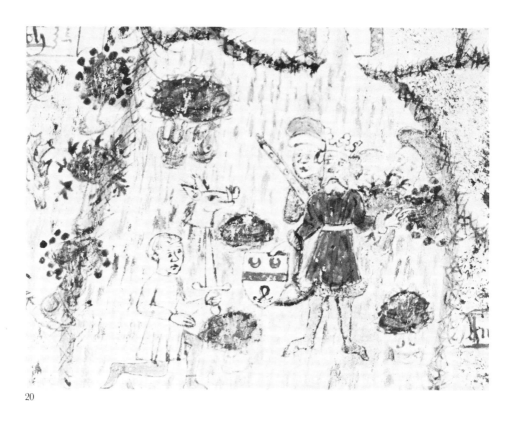

20

20 The Boarstall Cartulary, 1444

Parchment, ink, colour, wooden boards, leather bound 17.5 × 25 cm
Buckinghamshire Record Office AR.38/62/1

Compiled in and after 1444 for Edmund Rede the Younger of Boarstall, Buckinghamshire, the cartulary contains copies of deeds, privileges and other important documents concerning the Rede properties in Boarstall, a member of the royal manor of Brill in Bernewode. Its unique feature is a map of the township and its surrounding fields and woodlands, which is thought to be the earliest visual representation of an English village. At the bottom is depicted the legend of the Boarstall Horn, given to the forester Nigel by the King (Edward the Confessor in one version), for having slain a great boar in Bernewode. The Fitz Nigels were ancestors of the Redes and their predecessors in the Forestership.

21 The Boarstall Horn, 15th century

Animal horn, silver gilt mountings, black 57 × 26 cm
Buckinghamshire Record Office AR.38/62/2

One of a small number of surviving 'tenurial' horns, the Boarstall Horn passed with the office of Forester of Bernewode and land called Derehide in Boarstall. The giving of objects to symbolise the transfer of title or rights was common until at least the 12th century when written charters began to supplant the custom.

The Horn consists of two separate parts riveted together in the middle. There is a slot for a baldric or cord on the upper side, five centimetres from the rim. The mountings are of mid-15th century workmanship with scalloped edges and an incised decorative pattern.

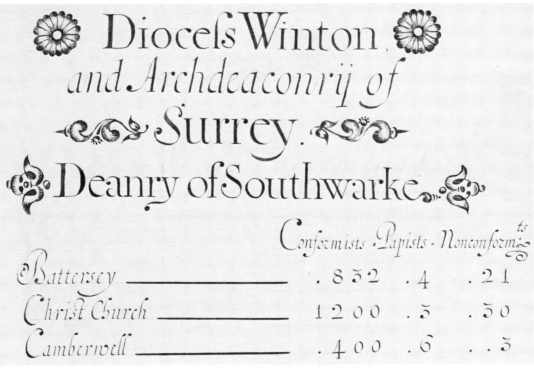

Dioce**s** Winton, and Archdeaconr**ij** of Surrey. Deanry of Southwarke.

	Conformists	Papists	Nonconformists
Battersey	.852	.4	.21
Christ Church	1200	.5	.50
Camberwell	.400	.6	..3

23

22 Aylmerton manor court roll, 1381–95

Parchment, ink 72×27 cm
Norfolk Record Office WKC 2/2

The archives of 'oppressive' institutions were prime targets in times of revolution and during the Peasants' Revolt of 1381, directed particularly against manorial dues and bond status, attacks on lawyers and the burning of manorial records were frequent. A gap in the series of court rolls for the manor of Aylmerton, in north-east Norfolk, is explained by the first entry on this roll, in translation, 'Aylmerton. The first court after the burning of the rolls carried out by the commons of the countryside who made a bonfire of all the rolls and other memoranda of this manor ...'

23 The Compton Census, 1676

Paper, ink, leather bound 25×37 cm
Staffordshire Archive Service: William Salt Library SMS. 33

In 1670 the Archbishop of Canterbury commissioned a survey within the Province to ascertain numbers of Anglicans, Nonconformists and Roman Catholics. The results, compiled from individual parish returns, were collated by Henry Compton, then Bishop of London. Engrossed in a neat classical hand and finely bound, the 'census' was bought by William Salt, the Staffordshire antiquary, in the 19th century. It now constitutes a major source for population historians.

24 Dunstable parish register, 1558–1749

Parchment, ink, vellum bound 24 × 34 cm
Bedfordshire Record Office P 72/1/1 (Dunstable)

Commenced in 1598 by John Willis, curate of Dunstable, following an injunction requiring the acquisition in each parish of a parchment book to record baptisms, burials and marriages from the beginning of Elizabeth's reign. Like a minority of keepers of these new records, Willis chose to reflect its importance in an imposing presentation. The title page contains a symbolic representation of progress through life: the font to the left with the word 'unde' (whence) and, to the right, the gravedigger's tools and a coffin marked 'quo' (whither). The central panel is suspended from a wedding ring.

25 Rules for North Dalton Poor-House, 18th century

Paper, printed 45 × 56.5 cm
Humberside Record Office DDBV 32/1

A printed table of rules for the maintenance of a poor-house serving a group of parishes around the East Yorkshire town of North Dalton. From the 16th century the care of the poor became the statutory responsibility of the parish. A variety of attempts to reduce the burden on the ratepayer included legislation enabling parishes to group together in a union with a single poor-house.

The bill of fare was a constant subject for discussion by administrators, reflecting the balance needed between economy and humanity.

26,27 Pauper Badges, Fletching, 18th century

Cloth 11×9 cm (each)
East Sussex Record Office A 2714

Badges of red or blue cloth, bearing a large Roman P preceded by the initial of the name of the parish administering relief, were authorised by Parliament in 1697. They were to be worn on the right sleeve of the recipient of aid. The Act remained in force until 1810.

These badges were found among the papers of John Holroyd, 1st Earl of Sheffield (1735-1821), who took a great interest in the problems of poverty in Fletching, East Sussex, where his seat of Sheffield Park was situated.

28 Making Cider, Sutton, 1930s

Black and white photograph
West Sussex Record Office. Garland collection (unnumbered)

Apples being broken up for cider in a mechanically driven crusher, near Sutton in Sussex, an area in which cider has been made for centuries. The crushed fruit, put into hessian bags, was then squeezed in a hand-operated screw-press and the juice fermented.

One of a series of photographs by George Garland, a professional photographer active in the Petworth area of Sussex for over 50 years. He was particularly interested in recording dying crafts.

29 Pimp-making, Petworth, *c.* 1933

Black and white photograph
West Sussex Record Office. Garland collection Neg.no.30041

Walter Luttman making pimps at Oldham, Foxhill, Petworth in Sussex. The pimps are small bundles of chopped wood used for lighting fires. The wood is being aligned on a 'horse' prior to being bound with a withe.

From the George Garland collection (see above).

30 Barming parish register, 1757–1812

Paper, ink 16.5×21 cm
Kent Archives Office P16/1/4

From its beginnings (see 24), the parish register assumed a central importance among locally kept documents. It was the most basic, and for many the only, record of arrival into and departure from the world. In the 18th century a printed format was adopted, reducing opportunities for individualism on the part of the incumbent or clerk who made the entries.

Occasionally, however, a determined writer would break through the conventions. The Reverend Mark Noble, rector of Barming in Kent from 1786 to 1827, turned his burial register into a detailed account of the lives and characters of his parishioners, describing in some cases the occasion of their deaths, in others incidents illustrating their nature or sufferings.

31 'Features of Wortham', 1870

Paper, ink, watercolour, leather bound, gold tooled binding 27 × 33.5 cm
Suffolk Record Office HA 11/A13/10

'A few parochial features of Wortham from A.D. 1828 to 1870' compiled by the Reverend Richard Cobbold, novelist and incumbent of that Suffolk parish from 1827 until his death in 1877. Cobbold's care and devotion to his flock are clearly reflected in this series of 105 short handwritten descriptions, accompanied by his primitive but highly evocative portraits. The descriptions, often touched with humour and pity, are perceptive, honest and intensely human. Together they form an almost unique social document.

This volume, one of several variants compiled by Cobbold, was inscribed and presented to the 2nd Earl of Stradbrooke, Lord Lieutenant of Suffolk, in 1870.

32 Ismay's Diary, Mirfield, 18th century

Paper, ink 11 × 17 cm
West Yorkshire Archive Service D1/192

'Diary of events, etc', kept by the Reverend Joseph Ismay between 1722 and 1763, during his time as vicar of Mirfield, West Yorkshire. Ismay had a keen interest in every aspect of his locality and combined in his diary a record of local and national events, including the earthquake which shook the village in 1738, with a survey of the plants, agriculture and buildings in the parish and a record of local market prices.

Ismay was one of a number of scholar parsons who were active throughout the 18th and 19th centuries and were an important influence on the development of the study of local history.

33 Grosmont mop fair broadsheet, 1847

Paper, printed 22 × 28.5 cm
Gwent Record Office D.361.F/P.4.123

A broadsheet advertising a typical 'mop' or hiring fair at Grosmont, an ancient borough on the Monmouthshire/Herefordshire border. Mop fairs were traditionally held in country towns during the month of May, when farmers would take on servants and labourers for the coming year. They also provided an opportunity for local sports and jollification and for the local printer to exploit the full range of his typefaces.

34 Village Customs, Ford, 18th century

Paper, ink 21 × 32 cm
Northumberland Record Office NRO.1216/Box 14/15

The survival and longevity of localised customs became a preoccupation of late 18th and 19th century gentlemen-scholars, many of whom recorded their 'discoveries' in journals such as the *Gentleman's Magazine*. This anonymous note of the 'peculiar customs' reputedly practised in one Northumberland village may, as was often the case, project a more vigorous 'folk-life' than probably prevailed. However, evidence of country customs is always rare and its survival a matter of interest to modern folklorists.

35

35 Plough Stotts, Yorkshire, early 19th century

Paper, ink, watercolour, leather bound 49×36 cm
West Yorkshire Archive Service: Yorkshire Archaeological Society MS1000

A water-colour by George Walker of Killingbeck, Yorkshire (1781–1856), showing Plough Stotts, the Plough Monday tradition of rustic theatricals, involving, here, the conductors of the plough, the plough-driver with fool's bladder, the fiddler, a clown in woman's dress and Captain Canf Tail, the leader of the troupe.

Walker, a landscape painter, was commissioned to produce a series of paintings on Yorkshire life by the Leeds booksellers, Robinson and Son, who published them as *The Costume of Yorkshire* in 1814 with accompanying English and French text.

36 Fairlop Fair, 1815

Paper, print, colour 35×23 cm
Essex Record Office. Mint Portfolio: Great Ilford

A hand-coloured engraving of festivities at the celebrated Fairlop Fair in Hainault Forest to the east of London. Originally founded as an annual celebration on the completion of the Midsummer rent collection for a local landowner, it developed by the early 18th century into a popular and prestigious occasion, which attracted large crowds. It survived until 1843 despite earlier attempts to suppress it on the grounds of its 'great encouragement of vice and immorality'.

37 Docking Union Association poster, 1871

Paper, printed 75×50 cm
Norfolk Record Office SO 17/3

The other side of the authoritarian face of the Victorian poor law was the paternal. The Docking Union Association, in north-west Norfolk, was formed in 1840 as an interesting attempt to promote 'the encouragement of Industry and Frugality and for rewarding good conduct amongst Servants, Labourers and Cottagers within the Docking Union'. Subscriptions from landowners and clergymen provided money for prizes and an annual flower show.
The Association was wound up in 1873 because it was thought to be no longer necessary.

38,39,40 Parents' letters, Hope under Dinmore School, 1888

Paper, ink 11×18 cm (each)
Hereford and Worcester Record Office A63/IV/HB/591

The extension of elementary schooling throughout the whole community in the last quarter of the 19th century provided unprecedented opportunities but it also presented problems to families who for generations had come to rely upon their children as a source of cheap labour at certain times of the year. The withholding of children from school at harvest and other times was a regular feature of late Victorian schooling.
Hope under Dinmore School was founded in the 1860s as a voluntary school for children on the Hampton Court Estate of the Arkwright family. The letters explaining the children's absences were kept by John Arkwright.

41 Strike handbill, Gawcott, 1867

Paper, printed 19×25.5 cm
Buckinghamshire Record Office D/X 591/4

The strike of agricultural labourers in the hamlet of Gawcott, Buckinghamshire, in the spring of 1867 attracted widespread attention. Marx in *Das Kapital*, published that year, hailed the strike as evidence of a resurgence of 'the movement of the English agricultural proletariat', although the major upsurge of agricultural trade unionism did not come until five years later.
Access to the numerous local printing presses throughout the country was both easy and inexpensive for political and pressure groups in the 19th century. An enormous range of printed material survives.

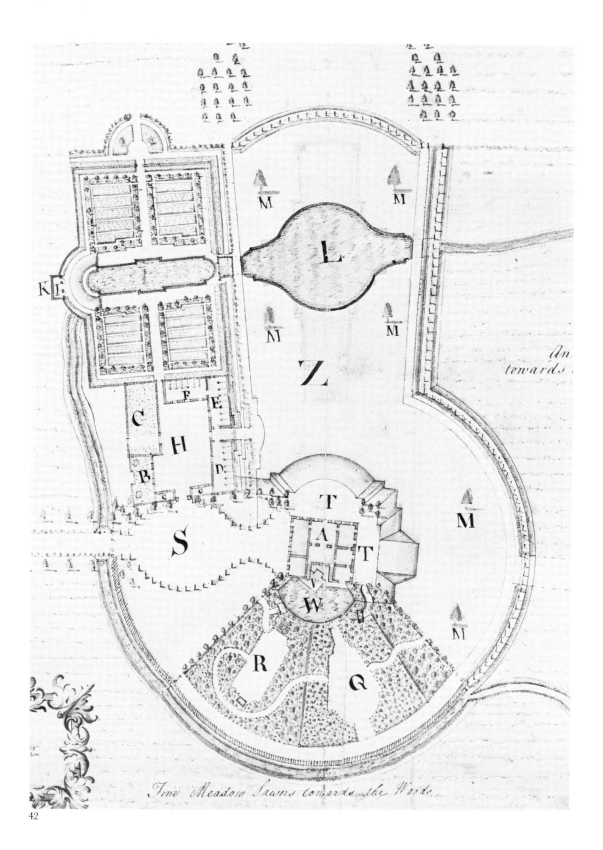

The Meadow Lawns towards the Woods.

42 Beaumanor Hall and Gardens, 1737

Paper, ink, colour wash, mounted on linen 74×103 cm
Leicestershire Record Office DG9/Ma/362/2

The house at Beaumanor in Leicestershire was begun for the Herrick family by John Westley, a Leicester carpenter, in 1725. The garden layout is probably contemporary and is a good example of the French formal garden, by that time on the wane in more fashionable circles, adapted and simplified for the smaller country house. It includes the popular elements of vista, avenue, wilderness, terrace and formalized use of water, all represented in modest form. The house was rebuilt in the 1840s to a design by William Railton.

43 Rousham House and village, 1721

Parchment, ink, colour 75×90 cm
Oxfordshire Record Office Cott.I/1

This map shows a typical open-field parish before enclosure, with its patterns of individually farmed strips or furlongs within the larger fields. Of particular interest is Rousham House, shown in the top right-hand corner of the map to the left of the church. Built in the late 1630s, it was landscaped by William Kent shortly after this map was drawn up. The formal gardens to the north of the house were removed to make Kent's 'bowling green'. Further north are the terraces leading down to the riverside. The New Garden to the north-west probably dates from the early 18th century. The large pond, changed to an octagon, later became part of Kent's 'Venus Vale'.

44 Audley End house and grounds, 1783

Paper, ink 104×98 cm
Essex Record Office D/Qy 8

A plan by Thomas Warren of Bury St Edmunds, of Audley End near Saffron Walden, Essex, in 1783. The grounds were laid out for Sir John Griffin Griffin on the basis of a scheme by Lancelot Brown. Work began in 1763. It involved the removal of the Jacobean formal gardens, the levelling of parkland and the planting of many thousands of trees. The course of the river was widened and altered and roads diverted. To adorn the landscape, bridges, a Grecian Temple and an obelisk were built to designs by Robert Adam and a Temple of Concord overlooked the scene from the east.

45 Garden design, Belsay Castle, 1792

Paper, ink 84×58 cm
Northumberland Record Office ZMI.S.69/1

A design by J. Robson for the landscaping of the grounds of Belsay Castle, exploiting existing natural features in the style of Lancelot Brown to create an artificial lake with islands and ornamental bridge within a range of 'natural' park and woodland. The improvements were not carried out but between 1810 and 1817 a new Belsay Hall in the Doric style was built to the designs of Sir Charles Monck, using stone quarried in the grounds. The excavated area was converted into a quarry garden in the picturesque style.

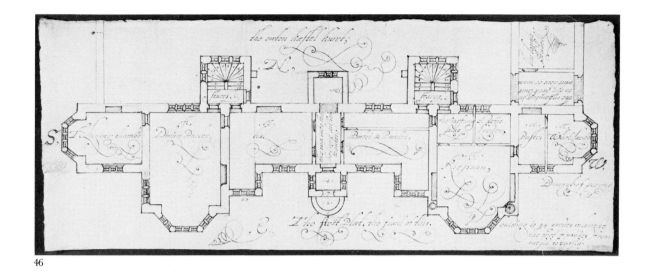

46

46,47,48 Plans for a house at Sheriff Hutton, *c.*1618

Paper, ink and colour wash 51×20 cm (each)
West Yorkshire Archive Service: Leeds District Archives TN/SH/A3/1-3

Three plans by Barnard Dinninghof for a house to be built within the curtilage and from the fabric of Sheriff Hutton Castle. Its owner was Arthur Ingram, a London financier and a secretary of the Council of the North. Dinninghof, a glazier by trade, had been responsible for the armorial glass at Gilling Castle in 1585. He offered to build the house at Sheriff Hutton, which was intended for occasional use as a hunting lodge, for £440. The house was eventually built to another design on another site, in brick rather than stone. Ingram later used brick again in his rebuilding of Temple Newsam in the West Riding.

49,50 Designs for ceilings, Newby Hall, *c.*1770

Paper, watercolour
49 48×65 cm   50 52×39 cm
Cumbria Record Office D/Pen/Newby

Two designs by Robert Adam for ceilings at Newby Hall, North Yorkshire, executed for William Weddell. Adam made extensive alterations to the interior between 1767 and 1774, providing a setting for Weddell's sculpture collection and, in the Tapestry Drawing-Room, for his Gobelin tapestries. The Drawing-Room ceiling, with panels by Zucchi, complements the tapestries. The second plan, for an unidentified room and probably unexecuted, is interesting for its cut-away sections in the corners and in the semi-circular end-piece, indicating coving along the edges of the ceiling and an apsidal end.

51

50a,50b Rheola House, Vale of Neath, Glamorgan, 1819

Paper, watercolour
50a 45.5×25.5 cm   50b 27.5×17.5 cm
Glamorgan Archive Service D/D Xfn 1 /11,12

Two views by the Yorkshire painter and mapmaker, Thomas Hornor, who came to Glamorgan in 1814 or 1815 as a land-surveyor and, while mapping local estates, produced, to commission, a series of views of scenes in the picturesque Vale of Neath. Hornor was later best known for his panoramic views of London (displayed to the public in the Regents Park Colosseum) and of New York where he died in 1844.

Rheola House was bought in 1800 by John Edwards of Lambeth, a parliamentary solicitor with Glamorgan connections through his first wife. Edwards later assumed the surname Edwards-Vaughan and represented Glamorgan in Parliament between 1818 and 1820. It was probably Edwards who commissioned Hornor to work in Wales.

The Romantic moonlit view shows the Vale of Neath as seen from the verandah of the House.

51,52 Part Books, Ingatestone, 16th century

Paper, ink, leather bound 29×22 cm (each)
Essex Record Office D/DP Z6/1,2

Two manuscript part books, the property of John, 1st Lord Petre, of Ingatestone Hall, Essex, whose name appears on the fine contemporary binding. Each book is the surviving part of a set for six voices. They contain a selection of secular French chansons and a large collection of Latin motets by English composers such as Tallis, Taverner and Byrd, to whom Lord Petre acted as a patron. Byrd was a regular visitor to the Petre houses at Ingatestone and Thorndon, where the part books would have been used by the family.

54

53,54 Country house album, Panshanger, 19th century

Paper, ink, watercolour, leather bound volume, gold-tooled binding
53 22×27 cm (book)   54 18.5×15 cm (drawing)
Hertfordshire Record Office D/Z37 Z1

An album of drawings, watercolours and verses thought to have been compiled by Lady Emily Ashley-Cooper (1810–1872) of Panshanger, Hertfordshire. It is typical of the output and pursuits of country house ladies of the time but its particular interest lies in a drawing by Lady Caroline Lamb, Lady Ashley's aunt. Executed about 1820 it is a more polished version of a childhood sketch in the Hertfordshire Record Office which is accompanied by verses:

> Farewell to England and farewell to frocks
> Now France I hail thee with a sweeping train
> Subdued at length I'll bend my stubborn locks
> And enter on a life of art and pain.

> Farewell to childhood and perhaps to peace
> Now life I sail upon thy dangerous stream
> And oh may wisdom with each year encrease
> And prove my Follies but an Infants dream

55 Household book, Cowdray, 1595

Paper, ink, bound in boards, leather spine 21.5×31.2 cm
West Sussex Record Office Cowdray Mss.18

'A booke of orders, and rules established by me Anthony Viscount Mountague for the better
direction of governemente of my howseholde'. The Montague household at Cowdray in
Sussex was a typically large and complex Elizabethan organisation which called for careful
delineation of rôles and responsibilities. The book lists more than 50 officers of the house from
the steward of the household down to the scullery man, setting out the duties of each and
concluding with a specification of the ceremony and procedure to be adopted when serving
dinner, and a table of fees.

56 Recipe Book, Erddig, Denbighshire, *c.*1685

Paper, ink, vellum cover 16×20.5 cm
Clwyd Record Office D/E/1203

The household recipe book is a common survival among country house archives, often
handed down and enlarged by successive generations. Most early collections also include
details of medicinal and cosmetic preparations. The quantities and nature of the ingredients
often reflect the size of the household and their access to dairy and garden produce.

This volume, from among the Erddig manuscripts, seems likely to have been used by the
Edisbury family, who built and occupied Erddig Hall in the 1680s, although the frequent
handing on of recipe books means that an origin elsewhere cannot be ruled out.

57 Servants' rules by W. E. Gladstone, 1840

Paper, ink 19×23 cm
Clwyd Record Office: St Deiniol's Library, Glynne-Gladstone MSS

Rules for servants at 13 Carlton House Terrace, Gladstone's town house, a late descendant of
the medieval and Elizabethan household rule-book (see 55). Gladstone's diary recalls that he
moved into the house on 11th February 1840. On the 14th February he 'wrote servants' rules'
and on the 17th was 'discussing and correcting house rules'. This document appears to be his
final draft.

58 Servants' wages book, Ashburnham, 1877

Paper, ink 21×32 cm
East Sussex Record Office ASH 2911

The organisation of the aristocratic Victorian household was a very strict and hierarchical
affair as is reflected in this printed register of servants' wages. Ashburnham House, near
Battle, Sussex, was, in 1877, the property of Bertram, 4th Earl of Ashburnham. The servants'
register shows that he employed 22 indoor female staff, headed by Mrs Battey, the house-
keeper, and 14 indoor male staff.

Pages of Beauty

59 Charter of King Wihtred of Kent, 699
Parchment, ink 35×15 cm
Kent Archives Office U140

This Anglo-Saxon charter is thought to be the earliest surviving document in any county record office in England and Wales. Written in Latin, it relates to the late 7th century kingdom of Kent, whose independence from West Saxon rule was re-established by Wihtred in 692. In the charter King Wihtred confirms the privileges granted by him and his ancestors to all the churches and monasteries in Kent, thereby freeing them from taxation. The witnesses at the foot of the charter include the Archbishop of Canterbury, the Bishop of Rochester and the Abbot of St Peter and St Paul, Canterbury.

60 Will of Wulfric Spot, 1004
Parchment, ink 39×54 cm
Staffordshire Archive Service: Burton Library. Anglesey 1

The will of Wulfric Spot, the founder of Burton Abbey in Staffordshire, comprises the second half of a document containing the confirmation of grants to the Abbey by King Ethelred II. It is written in Anglo-Saxon, while the charter above, in the same beautifully clear script, includes passages in Anglo-Saxon and Latin. Both are late eleventh century copies of earlier originals and form part of a series of eight contemporary abbey documents. The survival of such records for pre-conquest Benedictine Abbeys is rare.

61 Grant to Llanllugan Nunnery, Powys, c.1216
Parchment, ink, wax 15.5×25 cm (with seal)
Glamorgan Record Office CL/deeds I/3250

Llanllugan nunnery was founded as a Cistercian house towards the end of the 12th century. This charter, granted by Maredudd ap Rhobert, Lord of Cydewain, with the consent of his sons, Owain, Gruffydd and Hywel, is the only extant early charter relating to the nunnery and one of the few early 13th century charters to survive for this area of Powys. The main text is in Latin but the topographical details of the land granted around Llanllugan are given in Welsh. The document bears the green wax seal of Maredudd.

62 Building Agreement for Lyonshall Castle, Herefordshire, 1391
Parchment, ink 27×17.5 cm
Hereford and Worcester Record Office AH79

An interesting early French document for Lyonshall Castle, recording the agreement made between John Devereux, to whom Richard II granted the castle in 1390, and John Brown, a mason from Hereford. The proposed building work, which included the construction of additional rooms and a gatehouse with a portcullis, is described in great detail with exact specifications for the thickness and height of the walls and the type of windows to be provided. The agreement is of particular importance as little now survives of the original castle.

N HOMINE DÑI ·

gustino suscepta. eandem eccle
... fecit ...

EGNA
IH PPE TVO
mo ihu xpo s
mense aprilio s
IIII. kl' maias. r
VII. ego æthelber
filio meo eadba
ntione catho
optabile. Ho
aptu semp
qualiter p
panime
uel stabilitate salutis nre aliquid d
terre nre insubsidiis seruox dei
ma ...... debeamus offerre.

63

63 Textus Roffensis, 12th–14th centuries

Parchment, ink, colour, leather bound 17.5 × 24 cm

Kent Archives Office DRc/R1

The earliest register of the Cathedral Priory and Bishop of Rochester in Kent and the most precious of the cathedral manuscripts. A greater part of the volume was compiled in the early 12th century during the episcopate of Ernulf of Bec (1115–1124), and is written in both Anglo-Saxon and Latin. It includes Anglo-Saxon charters, laws and pedigrees, lists of popes, bishops of Jerusalem, and archbishops and bishops of English dioceses. It is thus a key document for the history of Anglo-Saxon England. The second part of the manuscript, which opens with a beautifully illuminated letter 'R', contains documents relating to the Cathedral Priory.

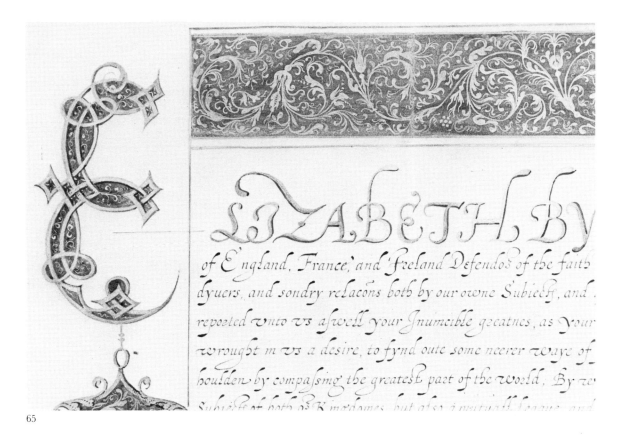

65

64 The Bury St Edmunds Psalter, early 15th century

Parchment, ink, colour 33×47 cm
Suffolk Record Office: Bury St Edmunds Branch E5/9/608.7

Colour plate II

The Psalter from the Abbey of St Edmund in Suffolk is arguably the finest ecclesiastical manuscript to be found in a county record office. Most of the volume was written in the abbey itself, probably between 1399 and 1408, and the exquisitely decorated letters bear witness to the remarkable tradition of illumination in the great monastic houses during the medieval period. The Psalter contains the Psalms of David, the Canticles, the Litany, the Office of the Dead and Canticles for festivals and is bound in with a contemporary Calendar, written at Norwich between 1398 and 1415.

65,66,67 Queen Elizabeth I's Letter to the Emperor of Cathay, 1602

65 Parchment, ink, colour 51×42.8 cm
66 Paper, wax 20×32.3 cm
67 Tin box 25×20.5×2 cm
Lancashire Record Office DDSh 15/3

The art of illumination was employed with a strongly Renaissance flavour to embellish a letter sent by Elizabeth I to the Emperor of Cathay. The letter, bearing Elizabeth's signature and Privy Seal and enclosed in a small tin box, was carried by Captain George Weymouth on his exploration to find a shorter route between England and Cathay. It requests the Emperor's protection for the expedition and proposes trade between England and China. The expedition was abandoned after the mutiny of Weymouth's crew in northern Canada.

68

68 Survey of the estates of Sir William Paget, 1549

Parchment, ink, colour, leather-bound 28 × 38 cm
Staffordshire Record Office D(W)1734/2/1126

A number of highly decorative estate surveys were commissioned in the middle of the 16th century following the break up of the large monastic estates (see 1). Sir William Paget acquired the extensive estates which formerly belonged to Burton Abbey in Staffordshire, together with the Trent valley estate of the Bishop of Lichfield. In 1549 his steward, Edmund Twynyho, drew up a handsome written survey of his master's estates. It is prefaced by a series of colourful coats of arms and introduced by elaborate strapwork headings. The volume is enclosed in a gold-tooled leather binding bearing the family motto: 'All for the best'.

69 'Speculum Nativitatis' of William Hickman of Gainsborough, Lincolnshire, 1655

Paper, ink, colour 16 × 21.5 cm
Lincolnshire Archives Office. Bacon/Tiny Grey Tin Box/6/1

A resurgence of interest in the ancient art of astrology during the Interregnum saw the publication of the first vernacular handbooks on the subject and the compilation of individual family horoscopes. The 'Speculum Nativitatis' was drawn up after the birth of William Hickman, the eldest son of Sir William and Elizabeth Hickman, by William Gregorie, 'one of Urania's yongest sonns'. It forecasts William's future complexion, manners, his wit and understanding, his general fortune, his wife's form, children, travel, tastes, friends, enemies and his death. Each section is delightfully embellished with coloured zodiacal signs and delicate cartouches. Unfortunately William Hickman died at the age of 25, apparently unmarried.

70 The Stanhope Pedigree, 1844–78

Parchment, ink, colour, silver binding 27 × 30 cm
Kent Archives Office U1590 F6

A magnificent example of Victorian grandiloquence and splendour is displayed in a pedigree reciting the history of the Stanhope family of Chevening in Kent from the 13th century. Compiled and illuminated by Catherine Lucy Wilhelmina Stanhope, daughter of the 4th Earl Stanhope, it also includes plates recording the birth of her own children and the pedigree of the Grenville family. Each text is decorated with an elaborate illuminated border of plants, insects and birds, all portrayed in rich and vibrant colours. The whole volume is encased in a heavily ornate silver binding.

69

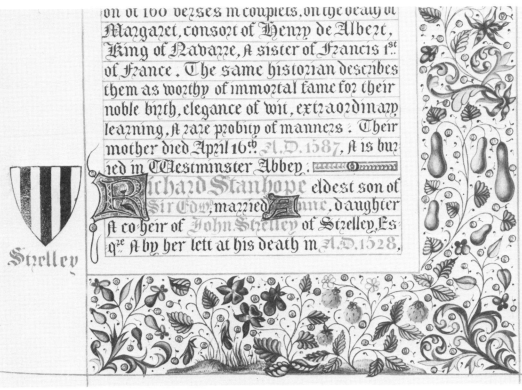

on of 160 verses in couplets, on the death of Margaret, consort of Henry de Albert, King of Navarre, A sister of Francis 1st of France. The same historian describes them as worthy of immortal fame for their noble birth, elegance of wit, extraordinary learning, A rare probity of manners. Their mother died April 16th A.D. 1587, A is buried in Westminster Abbey.

Richard Stanhope eldest son of Sir Edw. married Anne, daughter A co-heir of John Strelley of Strelley, Esqre A by her left at his death in A.D. 1528,

Strelley

70

71

72

71 Worcester Priory Charter *c.*1136–9
Parchment, ink, wax 28.5 × 58 cm (with seal)
Hereford and Worcester Record Office 705:134 B.A.1531/65(vi)

The use of the seal to authenticate documents was first realised in this country by the Anglo-Saxon kings but very few survive for this early period. The charter issued by King Stephen in the first half of the 12th century to the prior and monks of Worcester has a very fine early Great Seal. It is made of red wax and was originally attached to the document by means of a parchment tag. There has been some debate over the authenticity of this seal but it is now thought unlikely that a forged matrix could have been made during the lifetime of the king and the age of the charter itself is not disputed.

72 Licence to crenellate the manor houses of Mettingham, Suffolk, and Blackworth and Lyng, Norfolk, 1343
Parchment, ink, wax 39 × 42 cm (with seal)
Suffolk Record Office HA16/A1/1

An early example of letters patent issued by Edward III to Sir John de Norwich and attested by the Great Seal of England. The king's name and titles are written with dramatically enlarged initials and the authorisation by writ under the privy seal is noted at the foot of the text. Although the document itself has suffered some damage in the past the seal is in very good condition. It bears the traditional double-sided impression in green wax of the king in majesty on one side and on horseback on the reverse.

74

73 Creation of Baron Conway of Ragley, Warwickshire, 1625

Parchment, ink, colour, wax 78 × 76 cm (with seal)
Warwickshire Record Office CR 114A/261

In these letters patent, written three days before his death, James I created Edward Conway, his Secretary of State, as Baron Conway of Ragley. The document bears a superb example of a Great Seal in almost mint condition. It is also remarkable for its beautifully illuminated borders, depicting the royal heraldry on a colourful floral background. An elaborate gold strapwork decoration surrounds the initial letter J with a portrait of the monarch seated on the throne.

74 Lambeth Exchange Deed, 1197

Parchment, ink 60 × 40 cm (with seals)
Kent Archives Office DRc T54/2-3

Thirteen of the original twenty-one seals appended to this charter have survived. Eight of these are the distinctive elliptical seals of ecclesiastics, including those of Hubert Walter, Archbishop of Canterbury, Richard Fitz-Neal, Bishop of London, Herbert le Poore, Bishop of Salisbury, and Gilbert Glanville, Bishop of Rochester. The remaining five are baronial seals, including that of Roger Bigot, Earl of Norfolk. An almost perfect impression of the Great Seal of Richard I is appended to the confirmation.

The charter records the exchange of the manor of Darenth and the chapel of Helles in return for the manor of Lambeth between the Archbishop of Canterbury and the Bishop of Rochester, which today accounts for the residence of the Archbishop of Canterbury at Lambeth Palace.

75

75 Grant of land in Knebworth, Hertfordshire, 1411

Parchment, ink, wax 34.5×23 cm (with seals)
Hertfordshire Record Office 21929

The red wax seals of all five grantors of lands in Knebworth in 1411 have been preserved in remarkably good condition. The three left hand seals are the armorial seals of Sir Thomas Barre, John Lodewyk and John Durham. The fourth seal is that of John Ovyng, the parson of Northborough, Northamptonshire, and rector of Knebworth from 1368 to 1377 and again from 1381 until 1404. It bears the impression of his monogram. A device of clasped hands with a motto is shown on the fifth seal, belonging to John Clos.

76,77 Lease of Priory Garden, Hitchin, Hertfordshire, 1507

76 Parchment, ink, wax 36×41 cm (with seal)
77 Brass 4 cm (diameter)
Hertfordshire Record Office DE 112 B

The original brass matrix of the seal of Hitchin Priory has survived together with a lease of the convent garden and ponds, bearing a seal made from the matrix. The seal shows the Virgin and Child with the figure of a kneeling friar on either side and the royal arms of Edward II and Edward III. The Carmelite Priory of St Mary, Hitchin, was founded in 1317 by Edward II and both monarchs made grants of property to the house. The priory was dissolved in 1538 but traces of the original cloisters can still be seen.

78 Articles of Agreement, Ramsey, Huntingdonshire, 1629

Parchment, ink, wax 82×90 cm (with seals)
Cambridgeshire Record Office: Huntingdon Office R1/2/1

A spectacular number of seals, 169 in all, are appended to this agreement for the clearance of Muchwood Chase and the drainage and maintenance of Stocking Fen in Ramsey. Although some of the seals are duplicates most bear the individual impressions of the parties involved. The agreement was drawn up between Sir Oliver Cromwell, the uncle of the Lord Protector and lord of the manor of Ramsey, his son, Henry, Henry's wife, Dame Ann Carr, and the tenants of Ramsey manor. The signatures or marks of all the tenants are given at the foot of the document.

79 Royal Pedigree, 15th century

Parchment, ink, colour 18.5×220 cm
Hertfordshire Record Office 15857A

Poetry and artistry combine in this unusual pedigree which traces the descent of the Kings of England from William the Conqueror to Henry VI. The lines of descent are shown in red and a portrait of each reigning monarch is accompanied by a rhyming verse. The artist, however, has made no attempt to individualise the portraits. The verses are by John Lydgate (c.1370–1451). The verse for Henry VI mentions his coronations at Westminster in 1429 and at Paris in 1431, thus helping to date the pedigree. Lydgate also wrote a poem to welcome the King on his return from France at this time.

80 The Cornwallis Pedigree, 1560

Parchment, ink, colour 75×237 cm
Essex Record Office D/DBy F39

Colour plate III

From Elizabethan times landowners were commissioning herald painters to compile elaborate family pedigrees which were often works of great beauty and artistry. This pedigree was drawn up for Thomas Cornwallis of Brome Hall, Suffolk and Anne Jerningham, his wife, whose portraits in miniature are shown towards the end of the pedigree. At the head are four armed figures bearing shields charged with the arms of Tirrell, Tye, Braham and Bucton. 62 coats of arms are set amongst the trailing branches of vine, oak, honeysuckle and rose. The boldness of the heraldic painting, the delicacy of the floral background, the intricacy of the cartouches and the quality of the miniatures all indicate the work of an artist of unusual talent. The monogram, I.M., near the top centre of the document, is the only clue to his identity.

81 The Darell Pedigree, 1637, with 19th century additions

Parchment, ink, colour 130×600 cm
Kent Archives Office U386 F1

Sir Robert Darell of Calehill, Little Chart, in Kent, commissioned John Taylor to draw up this pedigree in 1637. John Taylor wrote to Sir Robert complaining that 'It is a very tedious peece of work and very chargable for I have doon it upon the best writing velam I could by for gold or silver ... there will be I am sure above 5 hundred coates ...'. The final pedigree, extended and updated in the 19th century, is 20 feet long and shows the descent of the family from Darell of Sesay in the reign of John. It incorporates an unusual series of fictitious portraits, deeds, brasses and sepulchral monuments. The latter were taken from originals in Little Chart church, which were destroyed during the 2nd World War.

82 The Vaughan Pedigree of Golden Grove, 1641

Parchment, ink, colour 145 × 549 cm
Carmarthenshire Record Office. Cawdor Collection

Colour plate IV

This magnificent pedigree was drawn up for Sir Richard Vaughan, Earl of Carbery, in 1641. An elaborate heading recounts that it was extracted from several pedigrees certified by Sir William Seger, late Garter Principal King of Arms, and enlarged by George Owen, York Herald, and Thomas Thompson, Lancaster Herald. The pedigree traces the descent of the Vaughan family of Golden Grove, in Carmarthenshire, from ten kings and princes whose full length portraits adorn the head of the pedigree. Amongst these colourful figures are Roderick the Great, King of Wales, Howel the Good, King of All Wales, Louis, King of France, Alphonsus, King of Castile, King William the Conqueror and Malcom, King of Scotland.

83 The Apreece Pedigree, 1753, with 19th century addition

Parchment, ink, colour 65 × 534 cm
Northamptonshire Record Office Map 1288A

A later example of an ornate pedigree compiled for the Apreece family of Lan in Brecknock-shire, illustrating the art of the herald painter in the mid-18th century. It recites the descent of the family down to Thomas Hussey Apreece of Washingley, Huntingdonshire. The coats of arms are represented by conventional painted shields but the painter has added a shadow to the charges on the shields to give a three-dimensional effect. The shields down to the 13th century are entirely imaginary. Although sections of the medieval genealogy may well be accurate, the tradition of reciting Welsh genealogies orally in families means that, in the absence of any documentary evidence, large sections have to be taken on trust. The final section of the pedigree was extended sometime after 1842 to record that the last of the family had died.

84 The Spry Pedigree, c. 1850

Parchment, ink, colour, silk backed and edged 60 × 161 cm
Cornwall Record Office DD:S 632

This pedigree was compiled for Sir Samuel Thomas Spry of Place, St. Anthony in Roseland, Cornwall, and shows the descent of the family and their intermarriage with the ancient Cornish families of Trenowth and Trejago. A panel on the left records that in 1839 Sir Samuel petitioned the Crown to be confirmed as Baron Fitzherbert, a title which he claimed through the Trejagos and the Cheynduits. The pedigree was probably drawn up in support of this claim, which was unsuccessful. Nevertheless the document is a fine example of the somewhat florid style of heraldic art, popular in the 19th century, and demonstrates the great interest which the leisured classes took in genealogy, particularly in genealogy with aristocratic connections.

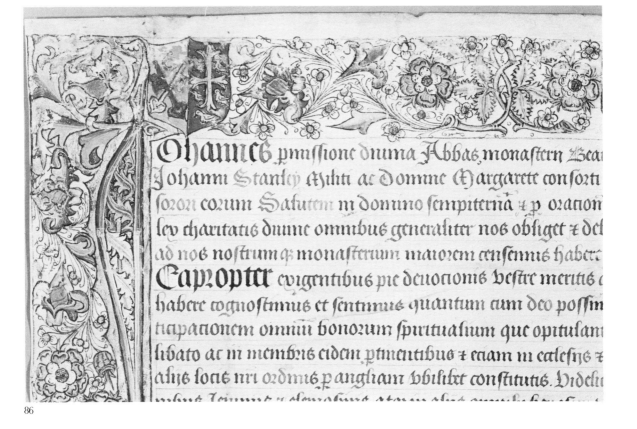

86

85 Illuminated chirograph, Durham, 1344

Parchment, ink, colour 34 × 39 cm
Cumbria Record Office D/Lons/L/Medieval deeds/S10

An unusual example of an early chirograph recording the gift of four manors in the county of Durham by the Archdeacon of Durham and the parson of Thorp Bassett to William, Lord Greystoke. The chirograph was a common type of medieval deed written in duplicate or, as in this case, triplicate on a single sheet of parchment. The document was then cut into three using an indented or wavy line which could be matched up at any future date to check for forgery. This chirograph is remarkable for its fine illuminated initial letter showing a coat of arms, bishop's mitre and crozier in red, blue, green and yellow.

86 Letters of Confraternity of Sir John Stanley of Handforth, 1527

Parchment, ink, colour 40 × 22.5 cm
Cheshire Record Office DLT/2173

An elaborate illuminated border surrounds this grant issued at Westminster Abbey. The decoration of foliage, flowers and 'Tudor' roses incorporates the arms of the Abbey, and those of Sir John Stanley and Margaret, his wife. The arms of Abbot Islip are also shown together with his rebus, in two places, based on a large eye. In this charter the Abbot and convent of St Peter, Westminster, undertake to pray, say masses and sing psalms for Sir John Stanley, Lady Margaret Stanley, and their children, John and Anne, both during their lives and after their deaths.

kgn
sdu
evis
Dou
posi
tuu
nsiq
oreo
gun
omu
tust
seu

at teteris pceuussis seu com
seu reputata existeu Atenu
quistum̄e ommu et singu
modo sint vyatum omnib

87 Deed of endowment and foundation of a chantry and obit and a grammar school at Week St Mary, 1506

Parchment, ink, colour 60×81 cm
Cornwall Record Office AD.405

A rare pre-reformation school charter granted by Dame Thomasine Percival, the wife of Sir John Percival, a Mayor of London. Written in English in a large vernacular hand, it is enclosed on three sides by a floral illuminated border in gold and colours. The upper border bears the arms of Percival impaling Westlake, Dame Thomasine's mother's maiden name.

The deed was closely modelled on that of 1503 for Sir John Percival's grammar school at Macclesfield. The grammar school at Week St Mary (1508–1548) was praised by Richard Carew in his *Survey of Cornwall* (1602) for the education of 'gentlemen's sons of Devon and Cornwall'.

88 Letters Patent of Elizabeth I, 1574

Parchment, ink, colour 79×52 cm
West Yorkshire Archive Service: Yorkshire Archaeological Society DD56 Add.1952/4

A fine example of the tradition of royal illumination used to embellish a grant by letters patent to George Lamplugh of Cumberland. A colourful portrait of the Queen adorns the initial letter while the heading bears the heraldic devices of England, Ireland and France, together with a rather cheerful dragon. An elaborate tracery of flowers and plants surrounds the text, stemming from elegant vases which are hidden by the plica. By these letters patent George Lamplugh was granted the properties of Thomas Hussey, whom he had 'stoutly and manfully apprehended in the field' during the recent rebellion in the north in 1570.

89 Letters Patent creating the Dukedom of Grafton, 1675

Parchment, ink, colour 72×68 cm
Suffolk Record Office: Bury St. Edmunds Branch HA 513/1/5

By the end of the 17th century the decoration on royal grants had become very ornate and stylised. This grant, recording the creation of Henry Fitzroy, son of Charles II, as the first Duke of Grafton, is one of five decorated patents issued by Charles II to bestow titles on Barbara Villiers, his mistress, on two of his sons by her and on Henry, Lord Arlington, father of the child bride of Henry Fitzroy. The decoration on each of the patents is similar but not identical. The initial portrait of Charles II on this grant has a different pose and expression from those on the other four patents. The borders, heavily embellished with gold and coloured foliage, bear the arms of England, France, Scotland and Ireland.

Urban Themes

90 Map of Chelmsford, 1591
Parchment, ink, colour 76×70 cm
Essex Record Office D/DM P1

This map of the manor of Chelmsford in 1591 is one of a series of very fine Elizabethan estate maps executed by John Walker senior and junior for wealthy landowners in Essex. It was commissioned by the lord of the manor, Sir Thomas Mildmay. The parish church, now the Cathedral, is shown at the top of the High Street, with the manor court house immediately to the south. The timbered Sessions House stands below this, with shops and market stalls down the Middle Row. The buildings are depicted in great detail and the skill and precision with which the map is drawn makes it an uncommonly reliable guide to the vernacular architecture and topography of the town.

91 Survey of the Manor of Chelmsford, 1591
Paper, ink, blind tooled leather-covered board binding 42×28 cm
Essex Record Office D/DGe M50

A beautifully written survey, companion to the 1591 map (see 90), giving detailed descriptions of manorial property, lands, tenements, customs, services and rents. It is not written in Walker's hand but it may be a copy of a volume prepared by him. Alternatively, at least some of the survey may be the work of Edward Moryson, surveyor, mentioned on the title page. There is no direct key linking the map and the survey, although the survey book provides details of all the buildings depicted on the map of the 'ancient goodlye manour' of Chelmsford, 'scituate ... in good and holsome aire convenientlie and well housed and well builte for timber and tile'.

92 Map of Maryport, c.1760
Paper, ink 42×33 cm
Cumbria Record Office D/Cu/Plans

Maryport, on the west coast of Cumberland, developed from a hamlet into a flourishing port in the middle of the 18th century as a result of the expansion of coal mining in the district, and because of the patronage and investment of the Senhouse family of Netherhall. Most of the coal was exported by ship to Ireland, hence the name Irish Street which appears on the map. This fine example of 18th century cartography shows many of the important buildings, including Netherhall, in elevation.

93 Map of Middlesbrough, 1845
Paper, ink, colour 58×47.3 cm
Cleveland Archives Department U/OME 8/9

The new town of Middlesbrough was created in 1831 by the 'Owners of the Middlesbrough Estate'. The Stockton and Darlington Railway had been extended there in 1830, and the original reason for developing the new town was as a coal port. However, the phenomenal growth of Middlesbrough from a population of 150 in 1831 to over 90,000 in 1901 was due to its development as an iron and steel manufacturing centre. This map shows a town with steadily growing industries, the most important ultimately being the ironworks of Bolckow and Vaughan.

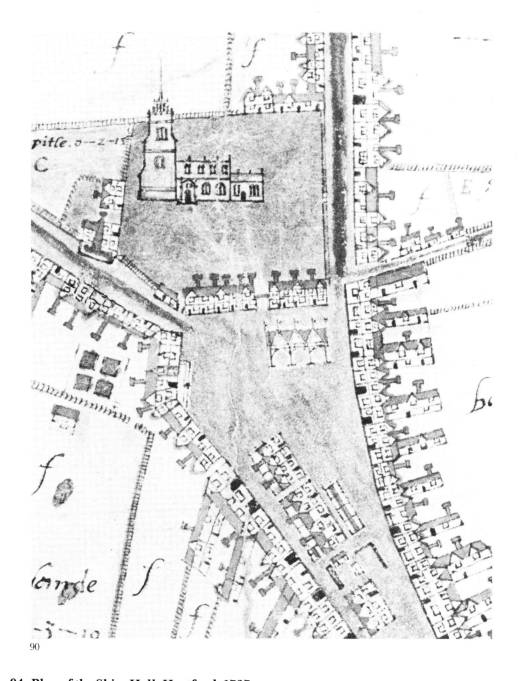

90

94 Plan of the Shire Hall, Hertford, 1767

Paper, ink 61 × 48 cm
Hertfordshire Record Office D/EP P11

In 1767 a successful petition was presented to Parliament by the Hertfordshire County Justices for the erection of a new Shire Hall, as the 'Sessions House' in Hertford was 'very ancient and decayed'. This plan, from a set signed by James Adam, represents the first scheme submitted to the justices by the famous architect. A second series of amended plans was finally accepted and the new building was completed in 1771 at a cost of £5,776. Repairs to the structure in 1788, costing £1,000, did not reflect great credit on the architect. The building still stands, although somewhat altered.

95 The first Bedfordshire County Council, 1889

Sepia photograph 43 × 30.5 cm
Bedfordshire Record Office CCV 33/57

When County Councils were established in 1888, as the administrative successors to the Court of Quarter Sessions, for the first time local government was placed in the hands of a body of elected representatives instead of magistrates appointed by the Crown. The first election in Bedfordshire took place on 24 January 1889. This photograph of the first Council, taken by Percy Graham, a Bedford photographer, shows an apparently severe, elderly group of men. The Union Jack sets the scene for a Council dominated by the old county establishment. One candidate who had run for election on the slogan 'we want men with brains – not magistrates' was not elected. The nobility, the gentry and the law were all represented, as well as local business and the professions, and there was one clergyman.

96 Berkshire Quarter Sessions Order Book, 1837

Paper, ink, leather bound 27 × 37 cm
Berkshire Record Office Q/SO 16

Cases heard by the Justices of the Peace at the Quarter Sessions were often recorded in considerable detail. The Berkshire Order Book recounts that on 29 June 1837, 'under the influence of strong liquor', William Budd, the long serving Clerk of the Peace, went into the court of Quarter Sessions sitting at Abingdon, climbed on to the Counsel Table and shouted and gesticulated at the court. When the clerical Chairman of the Bench remonstrated with him, Budd abused him and his colleagues in a colourful and personal fashion. The court was set to deprive Budd of his office after this episode, but the matter was finally dropped after an abject apology.

97 Tetbury Borough Charter, 1268

Parchment, ink, wax 15 × 19 cm
Gloucestershire Record Office D 566 T1/3

This charter was granted to the burgesses of Tetbury in Gloucestershire by Matilda de Longespee, who is depicted on the fine seal standing between shields of her family arms. It confirms to Tetbury all the liberties and free customs contained in the law of Breteuil, a model for a number of English boroughs, and exemplifies the charters of boroughs founded by mesne lords which never achieved royal confirmation or formal incorporation.

98 Hertford Borough Charter, 1605

Parchment, ink, colour, wax 93.5 × 90 cm (with seals)
Hertfordshire Record Office. Hertford Borough Records

Front and back cover (detail)

This ornate and colourful charter was the third to be granted to the borough of Hertford. For the first time the borough was to be incorporated with an elected mayor and common council. Details of courts, markets and fairs are given but the most significant change was that the borough was to become free, no longer owing service to the King. A portrait of James I appears inside the initial letter 'J' and the borough arms are featured in the centre of the top border. The remaining borders are beautifully decorated with flowers, fruits and lively hunting scenes. The Great Seal and the seal of the Duchy of Lancaster are appended to the charter (see 73).

100

99 Wallingford Company Roll, 13th century

Parchment, ink 14.5×158 cm
Berkshire Record Office W/FC 7

The Berkshire borough of Wallingford, incorporated in 1155, has left a fine series of early records illustrating many aspects of borough administration from the early 13th century onwards. A number of company rolls survive for the period 1227 to 1296. They list the inhabitants of Wallingford in trade groupings, including glovers, mercers, weavers, brewers and bakers, for the purpose of recording tax assessments on each individual. The assessments vary from 2d. to 4s., and the rolls are annotated with notes of the instalments in which the tax was paid, or evaded.

100 Tenterden Borough Custumal, *c.* 1558–1656, with additions to 1702

Paper, ink, colour 21×29 cm
Kent Archives Office Te/C1

This custumal is the earliest of several surviving custumals for Kentish boroughs. It records the rights and customs of Tenterden which was incorporated in 1449 and was the only corporate town in the Weald of Kent. It also includes copies of charters, ordinances and constitutions for government, with lists of bailiffs, mayors, jurats and freemen. At the beginning of the volume are copies in English of important documents, and some of the earliest entries are finely illuminated. The volume escaped a fire at Tenterden Court Hall in 1666, but was badly damaged at a later date and has been extensively repaired.

101 Cambridge Plague Accounts, 1647

Paper, ink 16 × 40 cm
Cambridgeshire Record Office. City/X18

These accounts cover a period of some four months when plague was rife in Cambridge. Funds for the emergency were provided by two townsmen and one of the Esquire Bedells of the University. Payments are recorded for fuel and refreshments, including strong waters, beer, sugar, saffron and treacle, for medicaments, such as plasters and salve, and for erecting isolation booths on the commons, airing houses and 'searching' potential victims. Watchmen were posted at the booths to ensure the segregation of the sick. The various precautions seem to have been effective as only nine deaths from plague are recorded.

102 Bridgnorth Chamberlain's Account, 1607

Paper, ink 15 × 39 cm
Shropshire Record Office SRO 4001/F/1/25

In 1607 the Lord President of the Council in the Marches of Wales and his Lady visited Bridgnorth with their entourage. This account gives details of the banquet prepared for them by the Shropshire borough at the total cost of £27 5s. 8d, an extravagance no doubt designed to ingratiate the town with the Council. The account records the provision of such luxuries as 'one gallon of Hippocras and ... other banquettinge stuffe sent for from Worcester to feast my Lady and her Company after dinner £2 5s. 9d'.

103 Settlement examination of Benjamin Taylor, 1802

Paper, ink, printed 21 × 34 cm
Derbyshire Record Office D661 A/PO 257

The Settlement Acts of 1662 attempted to ensure that financial responsibility for paupers would be borne by the parish in which they had last gained a legal settlement. The subsequent settlement examinations record the interrogations of paupers by local Justices of the Peace about their place of birth, apprenticeships and later careers, thus providing details of paupers' lives not found in any other documentary source. In this example Benjamin Taylor, born in Denton, Lancashire, spent 15 years from the age of 13 looking after 'fire engines' (steam engines) at a colliery near Rotherham. There, tantalisingly, his story stops.

104 Commemorative Medal for Fielden's Ten Hours Act, 1847

Silver 4 cm (diameter)
West Yorkshire Archive Service C353/831

One of the medals issued by John Fielden to his employees, shortly before his death in 1848, to commemorate the successful passage of his Ten Hours Bill through Parliament. Fielden was the son of a Tory cotton manufacturer and his experience of the excesses of factory labour at his father's mill at Todmorden in Lancashire led him to become not only one of the country's chief cotton manufacturers but a radical M.P. and an ardent disciple of Cobbett. The Ten Hours Act ensured that from 1 May 1848 a ten hour maximum working day applied to women and youths under 18. The commemorative medal, preserved amongst his political papers, depicts the ideal of domestic unity.

104

105 Framework Knitters' Trade Union membership card, 1791

Paper, printed 16×20 cm
Leicestershire Record Office 31'23

The framework knitting industry began in London but moved to the East Midlands in the early 18th century. The trade was fairly buoyant at the end of the 18th and beginning of the 19th centuries, but slumped dramatically after the end of the Napoleonic Wars. Its first identifiable 'trade union' was the Stocking Makers Association for Mutual Protection, formed in 1776 to promote a Parliamentary Bill to regulate wages. This membership card of the Ilkeston branch of the 'Fraternity of Frame-Work Knitters' is an early example from one of the many smaller local societies.

106 Hosiery Trade Union poster, 1938

Paper, printed 25.5×38 cm
Leicestershire Record Office DE 1655/8

The hosiery unions were badly affected by the slump of the inter-war years. A new threat came from the development of hosiery manufacturing regions outside the control of the unions, where wages were usually well below the rates established in the Midlands. In Lancashire, for example, few workers received more than two-thirds of the Midlands wages. The National Joint Industrial Council was successful on three occasions, in 1920–1921, 1936 and 1938, in resisting demands from the employers for a reduction in the bonuses paid, a considerable achievement in view of the problems facing the employers. The poster was issued during the last of the three campaigns.

107, 108 Women constructing the Haverton Hill shipyard, 1918
Black and white photographs
Cleveland Archives Department U/S/66

The Haverton Hill shipyard was built on 85 acres of land on the north bank of the River Tees and was opened in 1918. The construction of the yard involved the reclamation of marshland and the photographs show that much of this wartime work was undertaken by women. The Furness Ship Building Company, which owned the yard, housed its workers in a 'garden village' nearby, although this was later deserted because of pollution from the adjacent chemical works. The yard closed in 1980, leaving only one shipbuilding yard remaining on the Tees.

109 Philanthropic Society Register, 1788–1808
Paper, ink 21 × 32 cm
Surrey Record Office 2271/10/1

The Philanthropic Society was founded in 1788 by a group of gentlemen, worried at the large numbers of children in the City living by begging and crime. By 1792 the Society was maintaining several 'families' of children cared for and trained by craftsmen and their wives. This register, the first in a series, describes the social background and habits of the boys, many of whom came from the London underworld. The progress of each boy in the care of the Society is recorded, including apprenticeship and offences and details of their future jobs and family life.

110, 111 Philanthropic Society photographs, *c.*1891
Black and white photographs 15 × 11 cm
Surrey Record Office 2271/41

Following its move in 1849 out of London to Redhill, the Philanthropic Society's institution became a 'farm school' and was classed as a reformatory. Farm work was the principal occupation, although carpentry, tailoring and other trades were also taught. These photographs, taken to illustrate *Saved from the Wreck*, a description of the work of the Society published in 1892, show the boys at work at such tasks as milking, hoeing, reaping, basket-weaving, and in the smithy, carpentry shop and cobbler's shop. They also show the school premises, including the houses, grounds and ornate Gothic chapel.

112 Kingston Poor Law Union Application and Report Book, 1852
Paper, ink, printed 40 × 27 cm
Surrey Record Office BG8/55/3

A report book kept by the Board of Guardians for the Kingston Union in Surrey gives details of applicants for poor relief who lived outside the workhouse. It gives names and ages of applicants and their families, residences and trades, and describes any disabilities suffered. It also records the relief payments already received, the cause of poverty and any earnings. It then states what relief was granted. These records reflect not only the changes in the availability of employment, the trade cycle and the slumps and booms of particular industries, but also the effects of individual misfortunes such as blindness, age, insanity, rheumatic fever, lumbago and a broken leg.

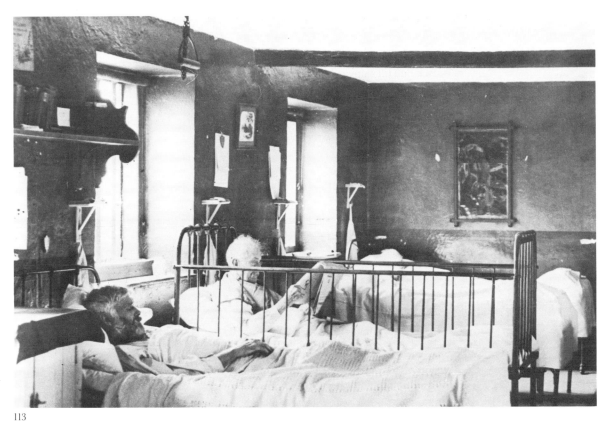

113

113,114 Petworth Union Workhouse, 1930

Black and white photographs
West Sussex Record Office. Garland Collection

Petworth Workhouse had been the parish poorhouse before the formation of Petworth Poor Law Union in 1835. These photographs, taken almost a century later, show the austere conditions inside the workhouse, despite attempts to brighten the room with flowers and pictures. Most of the inmates were too old and sick to work, although there was a certain amount of wood sawing for the able-bodied.

The photographs were taken by George Garland, a well known Sussex photographer, just before the closure of the workhouse (see 28,29). The building became a private school and was pulled down in the 1960s.

115 Plan of East Preston Union Workhouse, 1874

Paper, ink, colour wash 53 × 62 cm
West Sussex Record Office. Poor Law Records WG 9/56/3

The workhouse at East Preston was enlarged and rebuilt after the dissolution of the earlier Gilbert Poor Law Union and the formation of the new East Preston Union in 1869. The ground plan of the later workhouse shows how the strict segregation of the sexes was enforced. Work provided for the inmates included oakum picking or grinding bones for the men, while the women did the cleaning and sewing for the house. The diet included a large proportion of bread and gruel. When East Preston workhouse was closed it became a council home for the elderly, which shut in 1968.

116 Special report of the Medical Officer of Health for Jarrow, 1890

Paper, ink 22×34 cm

Tyne and Wear Archives Department T.W.A.D. T10/13

In a special report to a meeting of the Jarrow Corporation on 5 April 1890 Dr A. Campbell Munro, the Medical Officer of Health, commented at some length on the unsavoury and insanitary condition of the town. A particular cause for concern was the survival of no less than 1656 privy middens, which represented a constant threat to the health of the inhabitants. Munro referred also with some concern to the primitive nature of arrangements for cleansing the privies by the employment of night soil men, and the filthy and degrading character of their work (see 181).

117 Cholera Poster, 1849

Paper, printed 21×33.5 cm

Shropshire Record Office SRO 665/3/871

In 1848 53,293 people in England and Wales died of cholera. Such epidemics gave impetus to much of the social legislation designed to improve urban sewerage, health and hygiene in the later 19th century. This poster was issued in Shrewsbury by Thomas and Henry Blunt, chemists and druggists in the town, to give advice on the best ways of preventing and treating the disease. After comments on diet and cleanliness, they advise that a positive mental outlook is the best prevention: 'those easily alarmed are more subject to an attack than those who live in confidence'.

118 Design for a dispensary hospital, Sheffield, c. 1858

Board, pencil, watercolour 41×36 cm

South Yorkshire Record Office 20/B 1/3

This design for the rebuilding of the Public Dispensary in West Street, Sheffield, is thought to be the work of Thomas James Flockton, the son of the Sheffield architect, William Flockton (see 138). It was not successful and in 1860 the new buildings were finally completed according to the plans drawn up by M.P. Manning. However, in 1868 Flockton designed additions to the premises, then known as the Sheffield Public Hospital and Dispensary, and these were opened in 1870. In 1895 the building was renamed the Royal Hospital. It remained in use until recently when services were concentrated at the new Royal Hallamshire Hospital, and the old hospital was demolished.

119 Portable Font, c. 1900

Glazed earthenware 18 cm (diameter) × 20 cm (height)

Berkshire Record Office Acc.2314

Union workhouses provided Anglican chaplains and also allowed visits by nonconformist ministers. Children born in the workhouse could be baptised in the chapel there, or in an emergency in the wards, using a portable font such as this one found with the records of Newbury Union. A note of each baptism was recorded in the workhouse registers, many of which survive among the archives of Boards of Guardians.

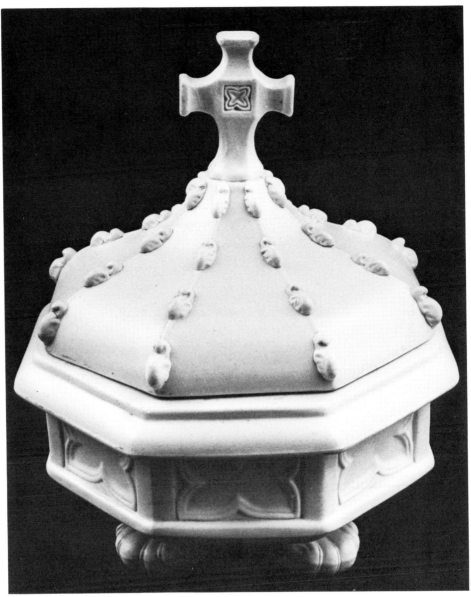

119

120 Map of Kilmersdon coal mines, 1695

Paper, ink, colour 61.5×49 cm
Somerset Record Office DD/HY Bx45

Surface outcrops of coal were being worked in Somerset throughout the medieval period but it was not until the 15th century that shafts were sunk to work the underground seams. By 1489 one pit in Kilmersdon was described as 'deep and dangerous'. This draft or working copy of a map of the Kilmersdon mines is the earliest known for any part of the Somerset coalfield and may well be one of the earliest for any coal mine in the country.

121

121 The Newcastle Coal Waggon, *c.*1820

Paper, ink, colour wash 43×29 cm
Northumberland Record Office ZMD.78/14

The growth of the Newcastle coal trade in the late 17th century led to the exhaustion of the riverside workings alongside the Tyne and the sinking of pits further afield. The potential transport problem was solved in the 18th century by the construction of wooden waggon ways. The coal was led along these ways mostly in single waggons drawn by a horse. This drawing shows a typical Newcastle coal waggon, with a pithead and riverside loading staith in the background. Each waggon held a Newcastle chaldron (53 cwt.) of coal and could weigh up to four tons loaded.

122

122, 123 Barrow Colliery Disaster, 1907

Black and white photographs
South Yorkshire Record Office 287/Z 11/1,2

Barrow Colliery, at Worsbrough near Barnsley, was sunk in 1875 and is still in production. On 15 November 1907 a cage containing 16 men struck a girder protruding from the shaft wall and the occupants were tipped out. Seven men were killed and the remainder seriously injured. These copies of two locally produced commemorative postcards show respectively a montage of portraits of the victims around the scene of the accident and a view of the funeral of some of the victims at Worsbrough parish church. They bear the marks of hurried production to catch the market while the subject was topical.

124–131 New Hartley Colliery Accident, 1862

124 paper, ink 13×21 cm NRO.488/A/3
125–131 Relics of James Amour (various) NRO.2567
Northumberland Record Office

The accident at Hester Pit, New Hartley, Northumberland, on 16 January 1862 was the worst disaster then experienced in mining history. Part of the pumping engine beam broke off and fell into the pit, completely blocking the only shaft, and 204 men and boys eventually died from gas poisoning. The dependents' relief fund attracted a nationwide response and this account book records the payments made to each household. Ann Amour was the widow of James Amour, the backshift overman, whose relics are also displayed. Following an official enquiry, an Act was passed in 1862 requiring every mine to have two shafts.

A Map OF CHACEWATER MINE IN THE PARISH of KENWYN and COUNTY of CORNWALL
The Lands of the Right Honourable Lord Viscount Falmouth.

BY S. MOYLE.   1813.   CHACEWATER.

WHL. ANN SETT

132

132 Plan of Chacewater Mine, 1813
Paper, ink, colour wash 62 × 41.5 cm
Cornwall Record Office DDX 397/91

Chacewater Mine, later called Wheal Busy, in Kenwyn, was one of the first major copper-producing mines in Cornwall. In the series of pumping engines which worked the mine, can be traced the development of the Cornish beam engine. Important engines to work the mine were built by Newcomen, Boulton and Watt, and Hornblower, and in 1811 Samuel Moyle, surveyor of this map, was the engineer responsible for providing the Chacewater Adventurers, the mine's owners, with 'the largest and most complete engine ever erected'.

133 Wharncliffe Silkstone Colliery Strike, 1893

Black and white photograph
South Yorkshire Record Office 400/B

This group photograph shows colliery officials at Wharncliffe Silkstone Colliery, Tankersley, West Yorkshire, with members of the West Riding and Cheshire Constabularies who had been drafted into the area to maintain order during the great coal strike of July 1893. It was the largest industrial dispute then experienced in Britain, involving some 300,000 members of local miners' associations, who were locked out when they refused to agree to a 25% reduction in wage rates. The men eventually returned to work in November at pre-stoppage rates after a period of acute deprivation.

134 Pen-y-fron and Rhyd-y-Mwyn lead mines, 1827

Paper, lithograph, colour 63×34 cm
Clwyd Record Office D/DM/219/92

Lead mining was an important industry in Flintshire from the late 17th century until the First World War. The mine shown in section in this lithograph was one of a group called the Mold Mines, taken over in 1823 by the mining engineer, John Taylor, and worked by him until 1845. Between 1823 and 1826 over £160,000 was spent in developing these mines and it was claimed in 1829 that the amount of water pumped from them – 8,000 gallons a minute – was the greatest in the country. The pumping was done by steam pumping engines and by water-wheels, several examples of which are shown.

135 Dye Recipe Book, 1761–2

Paper, ink, wool samples 24×45 cm
Wiltshire Record Office 927/11

From the early 17th century until the middle of the 19th, most of the fine cloths made in the west of England were 'medleys', that is cloths made of dyed wool of two or more colours which were mixed before spinning. So that colours of finished cloths could be accurately reproduced for further orders, clothiers recorded precise details of the weights and proportions of dyed wool mixed, and also of the quantities of dyestuffs used to produce a particular colour. 18th century dye books such as this are rare survivals. Before repair this one was a crumpled ball of paper and wool.

136 Account and pattern book of William Temple of Trowbridge, 1724–39

Paper, ink, cloth samples, board and parchment cover 18.5×30 cm
Wiltshire Record Office 927/15

Like most western clothiers in the superfine trade, William Temple marketed much of his cloth through a factor in London. The factor, Samuel Vanderplank, bought wool imported from Spain on behalf of his clothiers and Temple's book records receipts from London partly in wool and partly in money. Temple noted in addition what cloths were sent to London and kept small samples of his cloth to match if necessary. Temple was a clothier of some repute, claiming in 1744 that no fine fabric in the west 'comes up to the Elegance, Beauty and Perfection of my own'.

137 Elevation of Skipton cotton mill, 1784

Paper, ink 51 × 71 cm

West Yorkshire Archive Service: Yorkshire Archaeological Society DO 121/51

Skipton, in the old West Riding of Yorkshire, lies at an important junction for communications. In the 18th century it had a thriving market and well established businesses, and from 1772 plans were developing for the construction of a canal to improve transport further. Shortly after this, and perhaps as a result of the promise of improved communications, plans were drawn up for the erection of a cotton mill in the town. The detailed estimate, which accompanies this elevation, records a total cost of £1,000 to be paid by Lord Thanet, the landowner, for the mill's erection. The completed building was to be leased to a consortium for 21 years at an annual rent of £80.

138 Sheffield Castle Mills, c. 1835

Card, ink, wash 34 × 25 cm

South Yorkshire Record Office 20/B1/1

This drawing of Castle Mills in central Sheffield was made by William Flockton, the foremost Sheffield architect of his day. The son of a carpenter and builder, he was established in his own practice by 1833. The drawing was presumably executed for pleasure or as an exercise, since the mills were not designed by Flockton himself. Castle Mills, which stood beside the River Don at Blonk Street Bridge, were erected around 1825 and are typical of the industrial structures of their day. In 1868 they became part of Samuel Osborn and Company's Clyde Street Works.

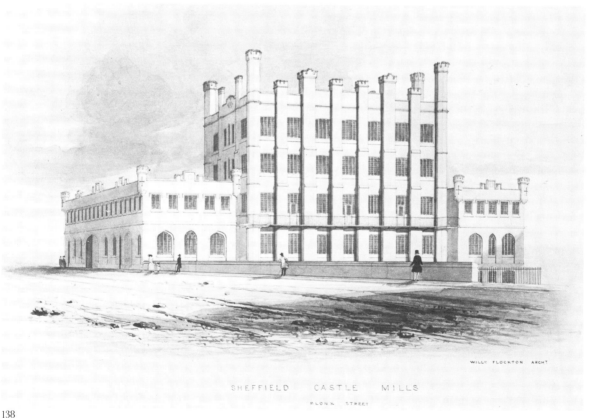

138

62

139 Preston mill rules, *c.*1850

Paper, printed 18×23 cm
Lancashire Record Office DDP

The manufacture of textiles became one of Lancashire's major industries in the 18th and 19th centuries. This broadsheet, produced by a local firm of printers, lists the articles and rules for Paul Catterall's Preston spinning mill and is a typical example of the regulations for textile mills in the county. The long hours are set out, 'from Six o'clock in the Morning until half-past Seven at Night, excepting Saturday, when work shall cease at half-past Four'. Breaking the rules incurred large fines, as for example in the 18th rule which imposed a fine of five shillings upon 'Any Person destroying or damaging this paper'.

140,141 Murder Most Foul, 1830

140 Paper, ink, printed 57×44 cm (poster)
141 Paper, ink, colour 48×38.5 cm (map)
Hampshire Record Office 19M68 PO178

A particularly gruesome murder committed on 8 November 1830 at Mortimer West End, Hampshire, resulted in the publication of this poster by the vicar and parish officers, offering a £100 reward for information. Charlotte Billimore, the victim, was an eight year old orphan in the care of the parish. Her assailant was discovered to be Thomas Miles, the nephew of the couple with whom she had been placed by the parish officers. An accompanying map shows the places referred to in the papers prepared for the Hampshire Assizes. However, Miles was declared insane and was not brought to trial.

142 Anonymous Letter to Gladstone, 1878

Paper, ink 13×21 cm
Clwyd Record Office: St Deiniol's Library. Glynne-Gladstone MSS

This threatening letter is from a collection of some 1,300 anonymous letters sent to William Gladstone between 1837 and 1896. The annotations on some of these letters show that they were originally selected by Gladstone or his secretaries from a much greater body of material. Many of them relate to the controversies over the disestablishment of the Irish Church in 1868–1869, the Eastern Question in the late 1870s and to Irish Home Rule. Many of the letters, such as this one, contain violent threats against Gladstone.

143

143 'An Arrest', *c.* **1858**

Black and white photograph
Suffolk Record Office S Ips 9

The original of this photograph appears in a fascinating album of work by Robert Burrows (1810–1883) of Ipswich. A successful landscape painter, Burrows developed in the 1850s a keen interest in photography and his surviving work shows a lively pursuit of the new medium. As an artist he was primarily concerned with composition and his work belongs with the consciously artistic photography of the pioneer days. This carefully posed photograph of an 'arrest' nevertheless achieves movement and drama and is by no means ineffective.

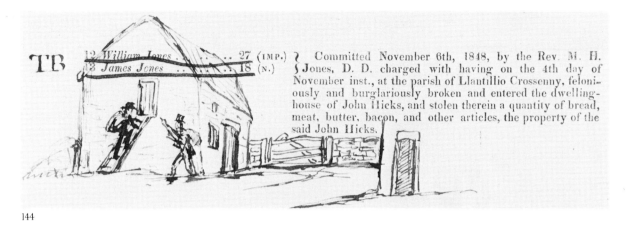

144 Calendar of Prisoners at Monmouth Gaol, 1849

Paper, ink, printed 21 × 33 cm
Gwent Record Office D.361.F/P.4.41

A highly individual calendar of prisoners, prepared for the Assizes by the Governor of Monmouth Gaol, has survived amongst the papers of John Etherington Welch Rolls (1807–1870), one of the Grand Jurors. The Assize courts, held locally before visiting judges of the central courts, dealt with capital crimes and serious felonies. In this instance each of the 60 cases is wittily illustrated with a delightful pen and ink sketch of the crime being committed. Many of the offences concerned property valued from £21 10s. to 6d. Five cases involved assault and four unfortunates had been apprehended poaching on the land of the Chairman of the Grand Jury.

145,146 Hodnet Lock-Up, 1831

145 Paper, ink 21 × 34 cm (petition)
146 Paper, ink, watercolour 19.5 × 31 cm (plan)
Shropshire Record Office SRO 2924/1–2

In January 1831 the problems of vagrancy, brought about by the increased mobility of labour, caused the inhabitants of Hodnet in Shropshire to petition the Quarter Sessions for a lock-up. They claimed that the town, which lay on the main road from Shrewsbury to Market Drayton, Newcastle under Lyme and the Potteries, was 'very much infested with vagrants and people of suspicious character'. The accompanying plan which they submitted illustrates the small cramped nature of these village lock-ups where offenders would be kept until they could be brought before a magistrate.

147 Ruthin Gaol plan, 1831

Paper, ink, colour wash 66 × 48.5 cm
Clwyd Record Office QSD

The county gaol at Ruthin, Denbighshire, was built in 1775 and later extended between 1802 and 1831 to house debtors, felons and female prisoners in separate areas. A detailed plan survives for 1831 giving an intimate insight into prison accommodation and living conditions. The felons' cells measured only six feet by seven and a half feet, although those for debtors were larger. Each cell had a small window and was lined with oak planks. The plan also shows the treadwheel installed in the 1820s (see 148–150). By 1837 the prison could house 58 inmates and in 1866 was extended again.

148–150 The 'Discipline Mill with Treadwheels', 1821, 1823

Paper, ink, colour wash
148 45×57.5 cm   149 43×56 cm   150 60×40 cm
Bedfordshire Record Office PP 3/4 and 5
Wiltshire Record Office. Police records

The treadwheel was invented by Sir William Cubitt in 1818 as a useful form of employment for criminals and a means of maintaining the harsh discipline of prison life. Many prisons adopted the treadmill at this time and it was not prohibited nationally until 1899.

A 'discipline mill with treadwheels' was constructed at Bedford House of Correction in 1821. It was designed by a London architect, John Millington, who was the County Surveyor and Architect for Bedfordshire from 1816 to 1825, and built by Thomas Elger, a builder of Bedford, and John Penn, a millwright from Greenwich. Two contract drawings survive to show how the machinery fitted into the building and how the prisoners were accommodated (148,149). Shortly after its construction the prison chaplain reported that the mill had promoted 'good discipline among the prisoners … and lessened considerably the difficulty … of preserving regularity of behaviour'.

The treadwheel at Devizes prison in Wiltshire was built in 1823 by the Bath engineering firm of G. and H. Stothert. The plans include an elevation showing the prisoners at work on the wheel (150). Later in the century the prison rules state that healthy prisoners were expected to do eight hours work daily on the wheel for the first three months of their sentence, a period which was gradually reduced to three hours a day after the first year of imprisonment.

151 Ruthin Gaol dietary, c.1850

Paper, printed 21×34 cm
Clwyd Record Office QSD

The poor and meagre quality of prison food in the middle of the 19th century is illustrated in a dietary for the Denbighshire county gaol at Ruthin. The main elements in the diet consisted of bread, gruel (a watery porridge) and scouse (potatoes and beef). The diet varied according to the length of stay. Prisoners confined for less than a month appear to have received no meat at all while those imprisoned for three days or less subsisted on bread alone.

152 Letter from a Hangman, 1880

Black and white photographic copy
Derbyshire Record Office D1500Z/Z1

As an executioner, William Marwood from Lincolnshire travelled all over the country in search of work. He charged a fee of £10 plus his travelling expenses and provided his own rope, straps and hood. This letter, making arrangements for an execution at Derby on 16 August 1880, also provides an example of the standards of literacy among adults of the period. Punctuation is minimal and spelling original and phonetic.

153 An execution, 1870

Black and white photographic copy
Berkshire Record Office Temp.Acc.52
(Thames Valley Police Museum D28:DB.3)

The hanging of John Jones alias Owens at Aylesbury Prison on 8 August 1870 provoked considerable interest in the popular press. Jones, described as 'a wild dissolute blacksmith', had been found guilty of the brutal murder of a family of seven at a remote cottage near Denham in Buckinghamshire. The full details of the crime and sentence were published in prose and verse as broadsheets and included this sketch of the execution as 'the cap was then drawn over his face, the rope adjusted, and the wretched criminal was launched into eternity'.

154 Report on Counterfeiters, 1615

Paper, ink 20 × 31 cm
Hampshire Record Office 44M69

A nationwide network of counterfeiters and other malefactors is revealed in this report drawn up by John Newbolt, the Governor of the House of Correction at Winchester, for the information of the county magistrates. Based on the confessions of prisoners and other sources, it contains graphic descriptions of the appearances and occupations of counterfeiters, 'fensing Kenes' (receivers of stolen goods), 'gamesters alias cheaters that live in London and come into the Cuntry at Fayres to deceave people of their mony with false dice and Cardes' and 'Foysts alias pickpocketts'. The report concludes with a glossary of 'Canting wordes' used by the community of thieves.

155, 156 Westminster Sessions Roll, 1620

Parchment, ink
155 38 × 60 cm (length of largest item)   156 37 × 8 cm (each item)
Greater London Record Office WJ/SR (NS) 2

This Sessions Roll for 1620 is one of a series of approximately 6,000 rolls for the county of Middlesex and the City of Westminster, dating from 1549 to December 1971, when the Quarter Sessions were replaced by the Crown Courts. The roll contains the legal records for the Session of the Peace for Westminster held in April 1620 and includes indictments, recognizances, writs and jury panels, all filed on a thong and wrapped around by the largest document.

Although similar records exist for the other county quarter sessions, the series for Middlesex and Westminster is thought to be one of the largest collections in the country.

157–161 Middlesex and Westminster Sessions Papers, 1644–90

Paper, ink
157 16 × 20 cm WJ/SP. 1645/17
158 19 × 30 cm MJ/SP. 1687/May/1
159 19 × 31 cm MJ/SP. 1686/Jy/1
160 20 × 30 cm WJ/SP. 1644
161 19 × 24 cm WJ/SP. 1690/Jy/17
Greater London Record Office

The many bundles of miscellaneous papers arising out of the work of the court of Quarter Sessions reflect the multifarious nature of the work of the Justices of the Peace, who presided at the courts. The selection of papers displayed includes a petition for assistance in poverty and distress, a petition for the release of a prisoner, a deposition concerning an illegal religious meeting in St Giles, Cripplegate, an address concerning James II's declaration of indulgence in 1687 and a petition against the nuisance caused by hackney coaches in the streets of Westminster.

DATE OF COMMITTAL.	REGISTER NUMBER.
July 12 1861	*6278*

Name. *William Flint*

Description.
Age *29 years*
Height *5/7*
Hair *Sandy*
Eyes *Blue*
Complexion *Florid*
Visage *Oval*
Weight *131 lbs*
Trade *Worsted Cord Maker*

Where born *Pumpl. Manchester*

Last residence *No fixed place*

Married or Single *Single*
Religion *Protestant*
Read and Write *Imp.*

Offence. *Begging at Luton*

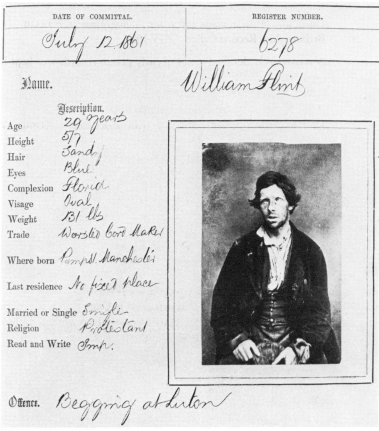

164

162 Reading Borough Watch Committee Minutes, 1855–9

Paper, ink 18.5×22.5 cm
Berkshire Record Office R/Sw 1/1

The Borough of Reading Police Force was set up in 1836, when it consisted of two Inspectors, two Sergeants and 30 constables, serving a town of approximately 18,000 inhabitants. A Chief Inspector was appointed in 1839 as the first in a line of Chief Constables heading the Force until 1968 when it was reorganised as part of the Thames Valley Police. This volume of the town's Watch Committee minutes records policy decisions and the day-to-day administration of the borough Force between 1855 and 1859. Items discussed include disciplinary actions against police constables who neglected their duty, promotion of officers, police clothing and matters of police pay.

163 Police Lantern, 1895

Metal, glass 13×17×16 cm (diameter)
Berkshire Record Office Temp.Acc. 50
(Thames Valley Police Museum)

This portable bullseye oil lamp, patented by Dolan and Company as the 'Crescent Lamp', was in use by the Home Counties Police at the end of the 19th century. It provided light for patrol work and could be used as a means of communication by signalling. The two looped handles at the back of the lamp allowed it to be threaded on to the police officer's belt when not in use.

164 Register of Prisoners in Bedfordshire Gaol, 1859–76
Paper, ink, printed, black and white photographs 31 × 42 cm
Bedfordshire Record Office QGV 10/4

A remarkably detailed series of early prison records was kept by Robert Evan Roberts, the Governor of Bedford Gaol. In 1857 he noted that habitual offenders were getting relatively light sentences because their previous history was not known to the court and in 1859 he sought to remedy this by taking photographs of the prisoners in his custody. The photographs were kept in a register together with a detailed description of each prisoner's physique, background, previous convictions and present offence. The importance of his work was recognised in 1861 by the visiting justices who gave him an allowance for his photographic expenses. The photographing of prisoners did not become standard practice nationally until after 1870.

165 Carmarthen Police Constable's diary, 1857–60
Paper, ink 17 × 21 cm
Carmarthenshire Record Office Mus.110

The daily events on the beat of police constables in the borough of Carmarthen are recorded in a series of eight diaries covering the period 1857–1870, of which this is the first. The early entries suggest, however, that urban life in Carmarthen was uneventful at that date, the worst crimes encountered by P.C. Harris in early December 1857 being an unattended cart and a housewife throwing hot ashes into the street.

166 Metropolitan Police Truncheon, *c*.1890
Wood, leather carrying loop 39 cm (long)
Hertfordshire Record Office: Miss Ann Pegrum

Wooden truncheons were part of the standard equipment carried by policemen in the late 19th century. This particular truncheon was issued to Stephen Toseland when he joined the Metropolitan Police Force around 1890. He subsequently rose to the rank of Sergeant.

167 Congleton Borough Police, 1890
Black and white photograph 21.5 × 17 cm
Cheshire Record Office CJP/9/68

A police force of sorts existed in Congleton in the early 19th century, four constables being appointed annually at the December Court Leet. However, the Corporation steadfastly opposed all government attempts to place its constabulary under the control of the Home Office until the Home Secretary's Report of 1889, which declared that Congleton was 'now the only borough of England and Wales having a separate force that does not maintain its police in a state of efficiency'. At that the borough council capitulated and the new Chief Constable, two sergeants and eight constables were photographed in uniform for the first time.

168 Handcuffs, late 19th century
Metal 23 × 14 cm
Berkshire Record Office Temp.Acc. 51
(Thames Valley Police Museum E126:EG.37)

A pair of handcuffs, with key, used by Berkshire police at the end of the 19th century. The uncomfortably close fit of the handcuffs ensured that they could not be slipped off.

169 Reading Police Force helmet badge, 20th century

Metal (chrome) 9×12 cm
Berkshire Record Office R/Boxes 997

This badge, in use by the Reading Borough Police Force until its reorganisation in 1968 (see 162), was probably introduced in the early 20th century. It bears the Reading Borough arms on a central boss.

170 Police whistle, early 20th century

Metal 8×2 cm on chain (45 cm)
Berkshire Record Office Temp.Acc. 53
(Thames Valley Police Museum)

During the 19th century wooden rattles were used by some police forces to raise the alarm in emergencies, but they were cumbersome to carry and did not always emit a clearly identifiable noise. They were replaced in the early years of the 20th century by metal whistles. This example was issued to a member of the Oxford City Police Force.

171,172 Slum housing in Seaham, 1934

Black and white photographs 22×17 cm (each)
Durham Record Office UD/Sea 123/7, 130/6

These photographs, taken in 1934 at the start of a programme of slum clearance near the docks and railway line at Seaham, show the crude masonry, small windows and cramped backyards of the working class houses. They were built for the first workers at the docks and on the railway at Seaham, which was developed by the Marquis of Londonderry as a port for the export of coal in the 1830s.

173–177 Slum housing in Sheffield, 1926

173–176 Black and white photographs 29×24 cm (each item)
177 Black and white photographic copy of Ordnance Survey map
South Yorkshire Record Office 263/Z 1/1–4

Although the construction of back-to-back housing had ceased in Sheffield by 1864, 16,529 of these dwellings were still in use in 1924. Until well into the present century a large population was concentrated in a warren of narrow streets and courts in the city centre. In 1924, following a detailed survey by the Medical Officer of Health, Dr Scurfield, the wholesale demolition of the city centre housing was recommended. These poignant photographs were taken in 1926 during inspections by Public Health officials, prior to rehousing the inhabitants in new estates on the outskirts of the city.

178–180 Cottages at Marley Hill, 1896

Black and white photographs
Durham Record Office D/Ph 92/1

An insight into urban living conditions and the resistance to change is provided in 1896 when the Medical Officer of Health for Durham severely criticised the sanitary conditions at Marley Hill, a colliery village near Gateshead. The Urban District Council responded with its own report, of which these photographs form part. They asserted that it was absurd to suggest that there was any lack of privies (three families shared each) or that the houses were badly ventilated. The deficiencies in scavenging which had also been noted were caused seemingly by an attack of influenza suffered by the District Council's horses.

173

181 Night Soil Men, *c.*1905
Black and white photograph
South Yorkshire Record Office 287/Z1/1

This photograph of the nightsoil men employed by Worsbrough Urban District Council in Yorkshire serves as a reminder of the noisome but necessary task of emptying earth closets in an age when few homes were connected to a sewerage system. As late as 1905 there was enough work to keep eight men and four horses and carts busy, despite complaints for a number of years that earth closets were insanitary.

182 Leicester housing plan, 1896
Oiled calico, ink, colour wash 67×51 cm
Leicestershire Record Office 23D67 (plan no.3639)

With the establishment of the Local Board of Health in Leicester in 1849 plans of intended new buildings were submitted to its surveyor for approval. A large series of over 200,000 detailed plans survives to date. The regulations regarding the size of houses and the amount of open space were laid down in the Leicester Improvement Drainage and Markets Act, 1868, and subsequent legislation. By the 1868 Act and the Leicester Improvement Act of 1881 the scale, size and content of the plans themselves were prescribed. When the L.M.S. Railway built its line through Leicester it also built a number of new houses to replace those demolished. This plan of 1896 shows one of these new houses, many of which are still standing today.

183,184 Hereford Co-operative Housing Estate, 1908
183 Paper, ink, mounted on card 58×37.5 cm
184 Paper, ink, colour wash, mounted on card 57×41 cm
Hereford and Worcester Record Office K21

These attractive plans show designs for housing to be built for the Hereford Co-operative Housing Society on the outskirts of the city in 1908. The Hereford Society, one of many springing up all over the country, was launched as part of a large-scale project of slum clearance and re-housing. Both the Mayor, Mr E. F. Bulmer, and Bishop John Percival were prime movers in the scheme and 86 houses in all were built. The plans were drawn up by Groome and Bettington, a local firm of architects, and were used in the Society's prospectus. They were later put on display at the Liverpool Town Planning Exhibition in 1914.

185,186 Peacehaven by the Sea, 1915–1934
185 Paper, printed, colour plates 21×28 cm AMS 5798/7
186 Black and white photograph C/R 9/10(1)
East Sussex Record Office

In 1915 Charles Neville began to create his utopian vision of a 'garden city by the sea' on a 624 acre site between Brighton and Newhaven. Many of the plots were disposed of by sale through his South Coast Land and Resort Company. Others were ingeniously disposed of as prizes in newspaper competitions. A brochure published in 1920 introduced the intending purchaser to the social, aesthetic and environmental benefits of Peacehaven. The reality was very different. A shortage of materials after the war led to the adoption of makeshift building methods and an aerial photograph taken in 1934 illustrates the patchy development, unmade roads and lack of drainage.

187 Blunham Rectory, 1873
Paper, ink, watercolour 65×47.5 cm
Bedfordshire Record Office X 497/20

The history of successive parsonage houses at Blunham is well documented in a series of glebe terriers, faculties and plans amongst the records of the parish and archdeaconry. The new rectory of 1873 built in yellow gault brick with polychromatic dressings, tiled gables and ornamental bay windows, was to cost nearly £2,000 and the mortgage debt remained a charge on the benefice until 1921. This plan is one of a series prepared by the architect John Usher of Bedford and shows the south elevation of the house, facing the garden and river Ivel. Blunham Rectory is regarded by many as Usher's finest work.

188 Moorfield House, Headingley, Leeds, 1920
Paper, printed, black and white photographs 25×32 cm
West Yorkshire Archive Service: Leeds District Archives Heppers 765

This rather pretentious suburban villa was built about 1857 by William Glover Joy, an oil merchant and alderman of the city. The sale catalogue of 1920, which has survived amongst the archives of a local firm of auctioneers and estate agents in Leeds, describes the rooms in great detail. The octagonal library is said to have a 'groined ceiling ... and a pair of cathedral glass windows depicting 'Literature' and 'Poetry', whilst round the room are carved Gothic bookcase fitments, behind one of which is a Secret Door opening onto a spiral stone staircase to the Tower Room.'

RULES

OF THE

LOUGHBOROUGH UPPER and LOWER
LANCASTERIAN SCHOOLS.

1. The Scholars are required to go to and from School in a quiet and orderly manner.

2. To behave respectfully to their Teachers, and strictly to obey the directions given them.

3. To take the greatest care of their Books and Slates.

4. Never to be unkind one to another, or quarrel, or utter a falsehood, and never to swear or take God's name in vain.

5. Parents are required to send their Chil-

190

189 Oxton National Schools, Birkenhead, 1852
Paper, ink, colour wash 89×54 cm
Cheshire Record Office SC 1/100/3

The school designed by Charles Reed for the National Society for Promoting the Education of the Poor in the Principles of the Established Church was in a gothic style calculated to appeal to the Anglican taste of the period. Reed was a favoured architect for fashionable middle-class suburbs around Birkenhead at this date. His design for Oxton is an interesting variation on the standard school plan. The infants', boys' and girls' departments form a long range of picturesque buildings reminiscent of a row of early almshouses or a small collegiate foundation.

190 School Rules, Loughborough, 1852
Paper, printed 28×45 cm
Leicestershire Record Office DE 641/1

The funds of the charity set up in Loughborough, Leicestershire, by Thomas Burton were used to support, among other things, two schools for 250 boys and 80 girls, established about 1830. The children were nominated by the trustees of the charity and were 'almost entirely the children of the lower classes', who were 'taught reading and writing according to the Lancastrian system'. These school rules were found inside the minute book of the Burton Charity trustees for 1849–1860.

191

191–193 Ragged School, Ipswich, *c.*1855
Black and white photographs
Suffolk Record Office K420/1

These photographs were taken by Richard Dykes Alexander (1788–1865), a member of the prominent Quaker banking family of Needham Market and Ipswich, and co-founder in 1849 of the Ipswich Ragged School. He was also a keen amateur photographer and raised funds for the school by selling sets of these photographs. They are a fine early example of the photograph as propaganda, moving and evocative, and their impact remains strong today.

194 Chester British School, 1869

Paper, ink, colour wash, wax 44×30 cm
Cheshire Record Office SC 1/40/4

A plan in elevation of the new school erected by the Chester British Schools Association to replace their former premises on which the lease expired in 1870. The commission went to one of Cheshire's leading architects, T. M. Lockwood, who, together with John Douglas, gave Chester its familiar 'black and white' townscape in the 19th century. The school was opened by the Marquess of Westminster on 1 March 1871. Girls and infants were accommodated on the ground floor, with boys on the floor above.

195 British Schools Manual, 1850

Paper, printed 14.5×22 cm
Berkshire Record Office C/EZ 39/50

The British and Foreign School Society continued the work begun by Joseph Lancaster to provide undenominational education for the poor. Its methods included running Model Schools at which teachers were trained, publishing standard lessons and handbooks, and encouraging the teaching of large numbers of children by the monitorial system. This *Manual for Schools*, published in 1850, set much emphasis on the training of monitors and includes a pull-out page illustrating the 'Positions of the Scholars' in response to verbal or signalled orders from the monitors, described in the text. Little attempt was made to encourage children to act as individuals.

196 Syllabus of St Stephen's National School, Reading, 1884

Paper, ink 20×24 cm
Berkshire Record Office R/DE/LN/33 [R/1700]

This table of reading books, recitations, geography subjects and object lessons for the infants and junior departments at St Stephen's National School, Reading, was approved by the School Inspectors on 9 October 1884 and recorded in the school log book. The volume shows that the school was quite large, consisting of 300 pupils divided into three infants classes and six junior school classes.

197 Embroidered Sampler, 1837

Linen, backed with paper 30×28 cm
Berkshire Record Office D/EX 238 Z1

School log books contain frequent references to classes in knitting, sewing and simple embroidery. This sampler was embroidered by Elizabeth Sandford, aged nine, while at Yateley School, Hampshire, in 1837. Worked entirely in cross-stitch and using four colours, it shows the alphabet, numerals and a quotation from Psalm 150: 'Let everything that hath breath praise the Lord'.

198 'The Tale of the Tub', 19th century

Painted glass lantern slides 8×8 cm (each)
Berkshire Record Office C/EZ 50/4

Victorian education was occasionally enlivened by the use of visual aids. This set of lantern slides, which has survived amongst the records of a school in Bracknell, Berkshire, depicts in coloured cartoon form 'The Tale of the Tub'. It consisted originally of twelve slides of which the first is now missing. Each slide was numbered and bore a caption along one edge, doubtless to be read aloud by the teacher. The eight surviving captions make it clear that this tale was in the tradition of the fanciful moralising stories popular in the mid-19th century.

199

199 Cambridge Coronation Sports poster, 1838

Paper, printed 25 × 76 cm
Cambridgeshire Record Office 463/Z2

A detailed and lavish poster proclaims the ambitious festivities to be held in Cambridge to celebrate the Coronation of Queen Victoria in 1838. A dinner of meat, bread, plum pudding and ale was served on Parker's Piece for 15,000 of the poorer inhabitants and Sunday School children. This was to be followed by Rustic Sports on Midsummer Green devised by Alderman Bridges 'whose vein for humour, fun and frolic is sufficiently notorious'. The sports included donkey races, dipping for eels and oranges, jingling matches, soap-tailed pigs, climbing greasy poles and grinning through horse-collars to see who could pull the ugliest face.

200 'Polish Salamander' Poster, 1841

Paper, printed 22 × 57.5 cm
Gwent Record Office D.361.F/P.123

This poster emanates from a theatre in Monmouth which housed a variety of entertainments from drama and music to this spectacular display of the strong man and fire-eater. The sensationalism of the poster is tempered by the footnote bowing to Victorian sensibilities: there will be no breach of safety or morality in the performance.

200

201 Poster for performances of 'Ghost!', 1876

Paper, printed, colour 33.5 × 47 cm
Shropshire Record Office SRO 665/4/495/2

From March to April 1876 the Music Hall in Shrewsbury put on twelve grand extra performances of 'Ghost!', the 'New Scientific, Musical, Literary and Phantascopic Entertainment which combines all the astounding effects of the Phantascope and Spectorscope'. The poster depicts the meeting of Faust and Marguerite in the garden with the demon floating in the air above them and illustrates the Victorian fascination with popular science and the supernatural.

202 Great Exhibition Poster, 1851

Paper, printed 32 × 51 cm
Humberside Record Office DDBD 5/53

The 'Great Exhibition of the Works of Industry of all Nations' at the Crystal Palace in London in 1851 was the first international exhibition of craft and industry ever held. The organisers were anxious that as many people as possible from all walks of life should attend, and urged the formation of local travelling clubs to charter trains to London for the event. This poster concerns the formation of a subscription club in Beverley, Yorkshire, to organise rail travel to the Exhibition for the working classes.

203 Ramsden Poster, 1852

Paper, printed 23×28 cm
West Yorkshire Archive Service: Kirklees District Office DD/RE/25

In the 19th century most of Huddersfield was owned by the Ramsden family. The occasion of John William Ramsden attaining his majority in 1852 was therefore of great importance in the locality. This proposed programme of festivities, however, so outraged some of the inhabitants that a public meeting was held 'to consider the aspersion' it cast 'upon their tastes, intelligence and character'. They questioned whether 'hunting a pig, climbing a pole and some other things announced in this list' was 'a fair indication of the culture of the people of Huddersfield'. When the day arrived it was reported with apparent delight that 'a continuous drizzle descended until the sports(?) were adjourned'.

204 Leicester Theatre Programme, 1850

Silk, printed, colour 32×46 cm
Leicestershire Record Office 31D56

The Theatre Royal in Horsefair Street, Leicester, was built in 1836 by the then County Surveyor, William Parsons. It was used for other entertainments and public meetings as well as for plays, on one occasion providing the venue for an exhibition of wild animals. Several well-known actors performed in the theatre, including Charles Kean, Henry Irving and John Toole, and in 1879 one of the first English performances of *Carmen* was presented there. This programme for a performance of *Richelieu* in 1850 is one of the few silk programmes to survive for this Victorian theatre which did not close down until 1958.

205 Folding fan, late 19th century

White ivory shafts, paper backed with linen, colour wash 35×21 cm (open)
Berkshire Record Office Temp.Acc. 54

At a time when theatres were lit by gas or oil lamps and had little ventilation a fan was not only a fashionable but also a very useful prerequisite for an evening at the theatre. This example is decorated with pastoral scenes of shepherds and shepherdesses dancing or playing the tambourine and hunting horn.

206,207 Opera glass and case, *c.*1895

206 Red leather case, conical, hinged lid, velvet lined 6 cm (diameter) × 8 cm (high)
207 Single expanding spy glass, white ivory, brass and glass
Berkshire Record Office Temp.Acc. 55

A Victorian opera glass, made by Dollond of London, with an expanding telescopic section and rotating lens rim for focusing.

208 Music Hall Song, 1887

Paper, printed, colour 26.5×36 cm
Berkshire Record Office Temp.Acc.34

One of a number of comic songs in vogue during the 1880s and published as a vocal score with piano accompaniment. The song, *Sister Mary Walked Like That*, describes the bride's progress up the aisle on her wedding day, in three verses with suitable mimes. It was sung with considerable success by Jolly Nash who is portrayed on the front cover. Several other songs and singers are listed on the left hand page and the whole score is bound into an album of music hall songs which were such a popular source of Victorian entertainment.

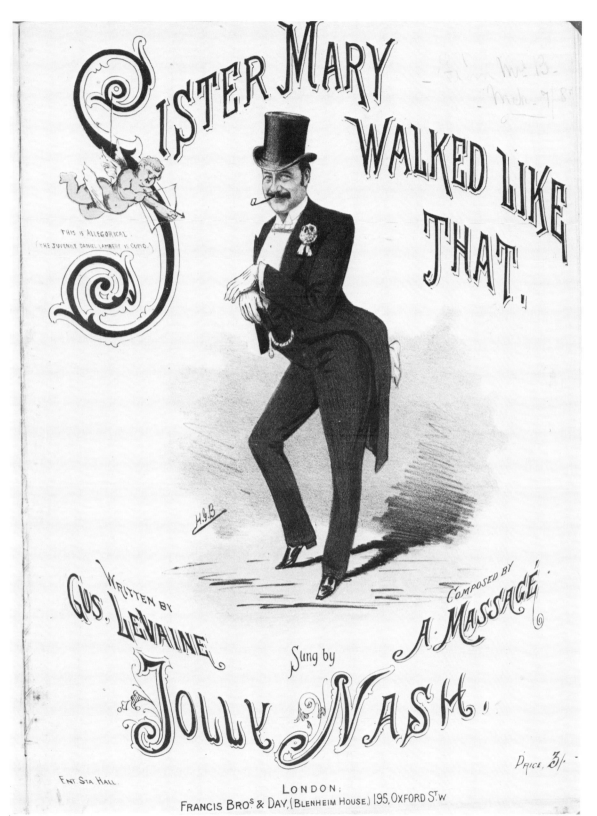

209,210 Musical Entertainments in Mold and Chester, 1882, 1903
Silk, printed, colour
209 15×22 cm   210 20×24 cm
Clwyd Record Office D/DM/403/2

Mary Maude Douglas-Adams (1856–1904) was a trained opera singer who had appeared in leading roles with several famous companies before retiring to settle in Mold, Flintshire in 1880. Thenceforth she employed her talents with great success as a teacher of music and in producing local operatic concerts. These programmes display her very professional approach to the local productions, the quality of which was extremely high. Her concerts in Mold Market Hall attracted an appreciative audience, but her production of Gounod's *Faust* at Chester the year before her death was probably her most ambitious.

211 The Mikado, Leeds, 1895
Silk, printed, colour 40×26 cm
West Yorkshire Archive Service: Leeds District Archives GT 211

The Grand Theatre and Opera House at Leeds, one of the few surviving Victorian theatres outside London, was opened in 1878. The programme of 1895 marks the re-opening of the theatre under new management, with a revival of the original production of the *Mikado*. The cast included Sir Henry Lytton, making an early appearance as Ko-Ko. He had joined the company in 1884 and did not retire until 1934.

212,213 The coming of the Railway to Northampton, *c.* 1843
Paper, ink, watercolours, linen backed 190×61 cm
Northamptonshire Record Office. Maps 1287 and 1292

The only way a landowner could envisage the effects of the construction of a railway across his land was to employ an artist to portray the imaginary scene. This technique of painting overlays so that scenes before and after could be compared had already been refined by Humphrey Repton, the 'landscape designer'. This panorama of Northampton in 1843 and the overlay showing the proposed branch line of the London and Birmingham Railway, indicates the effect that Bridge Street Station, ultimately built in a mock Tudor rather than a Regency style, would have on Edward Bouverie's meadows near Delapré Abbey.

214 Cautions to Railwaymen, 1831
Paper, printed 11×15 cm
Durham Record Office: Darlington Branch D/PS/5/2ii

The Stockton and Darlington Railway, opened in 1825 to transport coal from West Durham to the Tees, was the first public railway in this country and was used as a successful model for later promoters. It was based on the waggonways of Tyneside and introduced the locomotive engine on the advice of George Stephenson, the engineer to the Company. This notice was issued to all drivers, who were said to drive furiously across roads and run after dark without lights, and were alienating the goodwill of the mail coaches, which should have had priority on the post road.

215 William Huskisson and the railways, 1830

Paper, ink 20×25 cm
Staffordshire Record Office D260/M/5/27/6(46)

In 1830 William Huskisson, a prominent politician and former President of the Board of Trade, was in the midst of the enthusiasm for the new 'Railroads'. Two days before he was due to attend the opening of the Liverpool-Manchester Railway he wrote to Sir Edward Littleton, M.P. for Staffordshire, who was trying to acquire tickets for the great event. Huskisson was killed by a train during the opening ceremony.

216 William Huskisson

Black and white photographic copy
National Portrait Gallery

Photograph of William Huskisson, M.P., (1770–1830), taken from a portrait by Richard Rothwell, now in the National Portrait Gallery, London.

217 Rolls-Royce Cars, 1905

Paper, printed 9.5×14 cm
Gwent Record Office D.361.F/P.8.72

In 1902 Charles Stewart Rolls, the third son of the first Baron Llangattock, of the Hendre near Monmouth, established a company at Conduit Street, London, to sell imported cars. His dream to market a top quality British car came to fruition in December 1904 when he signed an agreement with Henry Royce. This booklet, dated January 1905, appears to be the first promotional material for Rolls-Royce cars. According to the Monmouthshire local taxation registers in 1905 27 Rolls-Royce cars were registered within the block of 30 numbers (AX 140–170) assigned to the Company.

218 Rolls-Royce 'Phantom I', 1920

Paper, printed 30×25 cm
Leicestershire Record Office DE 1518/69

One of the cars offered for sale by Hamshaw's Motor Garage in Leicester in 1920. The firm developed from a 19th century coachbuilder and proprietor with premises at 37 Humberstone Gate. In the early 1960s it moved to a purpose-built showroom and garage at Hamshaw House in Welford Road, Leicester.

219–223 Yorkshire Motor Car Company, Sheffield, *c.* 1905

Black and white photographs
South Yorkshire Record Office 399/B1/1-5

The Yorkshire Motor Car Company was typical of the many small motor body builders that sprang up in most large towns in the Edwardian era. At that time it was common for the more expensive vehicles to be supplied as a rolling chassis upon which the purchaser had a body of his own choice built. These photographs show that this was a highly specialised craft industry with hand-beaten body panels erected on wooden frames, usually of ash, and leather upholstered seats.

The Company's premises at the corner of Pinfold Street and Townhead Street in Sheffield were purpose built with showrooms on the ground floor and workshops on the upper floors. They no longer survive.

County Record Offices in England and Wales

This list gives details only of the principal offices administered by County Councils in England and Wales. For further details of branch offices and other local record offices see *Record Repositories in Great Britain* (H.M.S.O., 7th edn. 1982)

England

Bedfordshire Record Office
County Hall
Bedford MK42 9AP

Berkshire Record Office
Shire Hall
Shinfield Park
Reading RG2 9XD

Buckinghamshire Record Office
County Hall
Aylesbury HP20 1UA

Cambridgeshire Record Office
Shire Hall
Castle Hill
Cambridge CB3 0AP

Cheshire Record Office
The Castle
Chester CH1 2DN

Cleveland County Libraries
Archives Department
81 Borough Road
Middlesbrough TS1 3AA

Cornwall Record Office
County Hall
Truro TR1 3AY

Cumbria Record Office
The Castle
Carlisle CA3 8UR

Derbyshire Record Office
County Offices
Matlock DE4 3AG

Devon Record Office
Castle Street
Exeter EX4 3PQ

Dorset Record Office
County Hall
Dorchester DT1 1XJ

Durham County Record Office
County Hall
Durham DH1 5UL

Essex Record Office
County Hall
Chelmsford CM1 1LX

Gloucestershire Record Office
Worcester Street
Gloucester GL1 3DW

Hampshire Record Office
20 Southgate Street
Winchester SO23 9EF

Hereford and Worcester Record Office
County Buildings
St Mary's Street
Worcester WR1 1TN

Hertfordshire Record Office
County Hall
Hertford SG13 8DE

Humberside County Record Office
County Hall
Beverley HU17 9BA

Kent Archives Office
County Hall
Maidstone ME14 1XQ

Lancashire Record Office
Bow Lane
Preston PR1 8ND

Leicestershire Record Office
57 New Walk
Leicester LE1 7JB

Lincolnshire Archives Office
The Castle
Lincoln LN1 3AB

Greater London Record Office
40 Northampton Road
London EC1R 0AB

Greater Manchester Record Office
56 Marshall Street, New Cross
Ancoats
Manchester M4 5FU

Merseyside County Archives
64–66 Islington
Liverpool L3 8LG

Norfolk Record Office
Central Library
Norwich NR2 1NJ

Northamptonshire Record Office
Delapre Abbey
Northampton NN4 9AW

Northumberland Record Office
Melton Park
North Gosforth
Newcastle upon Tyne NE3 5QX

Nottinghamshire Record Office
County House
High Pavement
Nottingham NG1 1HR

Oxfordshire County Record Office
County Hall
Oxford OX1 1ND

Shropshire Record Office
Shirehall
Abbey Foregate
Shrewsbury SY2 6ND

Somerset Record Office
Obridge Road
Taunton TA2 7PU

Staffordshire Record Office
County Buildings
Eastgate Street
Stafford ST16 2LZ

Suffolk Record Office
County Hall
Ipswich IP4 2JS

Surrey Record Office
County Hall
Penrhyn Road
Kingston upon Thames KT1 2DN

East Sussex Record Office
Pelham House
St Andrews Lane
Lewes BN7 1UN

West Sussex Record Office
County Hall
West Street
Chichester PO19 1RN

Tyne and Wear Archives Department
Blandford House
West Blandford Street
Newcastle upon Tyne NE1 4JA

Warwickshire County Record Office
Priory Park
Cape Road
Warwick CV34 4JS

Isle of Wight County Record Office
26 Hillside
Newport PO30 2EB

Wiltshire Record Office
County Hall
Trowbridge BA14 8JG

North Yorkshire County Record Office
County Hall
Northallerton DL7 8AD

South Yorkshire County Record Office
Cultural Activities Centre
Ellin Street
Sheffield S1 4PL

West Yorkshire Record Office
Registry of Deeds
Newstead Road
Wakefield WF1 2DE
(comprises Bradford Archives Dept.,
Kirklees Archives, Leeds Archives Dept.,
Wakefield Dept. of Archives and Local Studies
and Yorkshire Archaeological Society)

Wales

Clwyd Record Office
The Old Rectory
Hawarden
Deeside CH5 3NR

Dyfed Archive Service
County Hall
Carmarthen SA31 1JP

Glamorgan Archive Service
Glamorgan Record Office
County Hall
Cathays Park
Cardiff CF1 3NE

Gwent County Record Office
County Hall
Cwmbran NP4 2XH

Gwynedd Archives Service
Caernarfon Area Record Office
County Offices
Shire Hall Street
Caernarfon LL55 1SH

The Friends of the Victoria and Albert Museum

The Friends of the V&A receive the following privileges:

Friends £15 annually

Friends (**Concessionary**) £10 annually for pensioners and full-time Museum staff

Free and immediate entry to all exhibitions with a guest or husband/wife and children under 16

Free evening Private Views of major exhibitions and new developments within the Museum

Quarterly mailings of Museum literature and News Letters

The opportunity to participate in trips abroad with Keepers from the Departments

Discounts in the Craft Shop and on exhibition catalogues

Corporate Friends £100 annually

Receive all the privileges offered to Friends, plus a fully transferable Membership Card

Benefactors £1000 donation, which may be directed to the Department of the donor's choice

Associates of the Victoria and Albert Museum

The Associates of the V&A are companies who pay a minimum of £500 annually, covenanted for four years, and who take a particular interest in the Museum and have a close involvement with it

Associates
B.A.D.A.
The Baring Foundation
Bonas and Company Limited
Christie's
Commercial Union Assurance plc
Granada Group
Charles Letts (Holdings) Limited
Mobil
The Oppenheimer Charitable Trust
S J Phillips Limited
Rose and Hubble Limited
J Sainsbury plc
Sotheby's
Thames Television Limited
Sir Duncan Oppenheim
Mrs Basil Samuel

Benefactor Friends
Sir Duncan Oppenheim
Mr Garth Nicholas

Corporate Friends
Asprey and Company
Bankers Trust Company
Bonhams London
Colnaghi and Co
Coutts and Co, Bankers
Doulton and Company
Goldsmiths Company
Madame Tomo Kikuchi
John Keil Limited
Ian Logan Limited
Madame Tussaud's
Mendip Decorative and Fine Arts Society
Barbara Minto Limited
Phillips Auctioneers
Societe Generale
South Molton Antiques Limited
Spink and Son Limited
The Wellcome Foundation Limited